DATE DUE

Growing Up with
SCIENCE®

Third Edition

16

Virus, computer–Zoology

 **Marshall Cavendish**
Reference
New York

CONTENTS

KEY TO COLOR CODING OF ARTICLES

EARTH, SPACE, AND ENVIRONMENTAL SCIENCES

LIFE SCIENCES AND MEDICINE

MATHEMATICS

PHYSICS AND CHEMISTRY

TECHNOLOGY

PEOPLE

Marshall Cavendish
99 White Plains Road
Tarrytown, NY 10591

www.marshallcavendish.us

© 2006 Marshall Cavendish Corporation
© 1987, 1990 Marshall Cavendish Limited

GROWING UP WITH SCIENCE is a registered trademark
of Marshall Cavendish Corporation

Library of Congress Cataloging-in-Publication Data

Growing up with science.— 3rd ed.
    p. cm.
    Includes index.
    Contents: v. 1. Abrasive-Astronomy — v. 2. Atmosphere-Cable television —
v. 3. Cable travel-Cotton — v. 4. Crane-Electricity — v. 5 Electric motor-
Friction — v. 6. Fuel cell-Immune system — v. 7. Induction-Magnetism —
v. 8. Mapmaking-Mining and quarrying — v. 9. Missile and torpedo-Oil
exploration and refining — v. 10. Optics-Plant kingdom — v. 11. Plasma
physics-Radiotherapy — v. 12. Railroad system-Seismology — v. 13.
Semiconductor-Sports — v. 14. Spring-Thermography — v. 15. Thermometer-
Virus, biological — v. 16. Virus, computer-Zoology — v. 17. Index.
ISBN 0-7614-7505-2 (set)
ISBN 0-7614-7521-4 (vol. 16)
1. Science—Encyclopedias.

Q121.G764 2006
503—dc22

                                                          2004049962
                                        09 08 07 06 05 6 5 4 3 2 1
Printed in China

CONSULTANT
Donald R. Franceschetti, Ph.D.
Dunavant Professor at the University of Memphis

Donald R. Franceschetti is a member of the American
Chemical Society, the American Physical Society, the
Cognitive Science Society, the History of Science Society,
and the Society for Neuroscience.

CONTRIBUTORS TO VOLUME 16
Chris Cooper
Tom Jackson
Emma Young

Marshall Cavendish
Editors: Peter Mavrikis and Susan Rescigno
Editorial Director: Paul Bernabeo
Production Manager: Alan Tsai

The Brown Reference Group
Editors: Leon Gray and Simon Hall
Designer: Sarah Williams
Picture Researcher: Helen Simm
Indexer: Kay Ollerenshaw
Illustrators: Darren Awuah and Mark Walker
Managing Editor: Bridget Giles
Art Director: Dave Goodman

Virus, computer

A computer virus is a program that is designed to damage computers. These programs are called viruses because they spread in the same way as biological viruses. A computer virus makes copies of itself on one computer and then infects many other computers. Viruses do not just stop personal computers from working, they can also damage communication networks.

Computer viruses have been around since the first computers existed in the early 1960s. They were first created by researchers who realized that software could be made to behave in a similar way to a biological virus. A biological virus infects a host and then reproduces itself before spreading to other hosts. Computer viruses work in the same way. Most viruses are short programs that are designed to stop the computer from working properly. Some viruses do not cause any noticeable changes. A virus program is also designed to spread itself to other computers. This happens most often through e-mail and Web sites. However, early viruses were spread by copying themselves onto floppy disks and other storage media.

Early viruses

The first computer viruses were studied in a controlled environment. However, programmers who wanted to cause trouble began to spread viruses to other computers.

By the late 1980s, personal computers had become common in offices and homes, and uncontrolled computer viruses were becoming a problem. Computers were not often linked to each other by networks, and the Internet was still being developed. Therefore, the early viruses were spread mainly on floppy disks.

Early viruses were small pieces of code embedded in a common program, such as a game. The viruses spread slowly as people shared the programs with friends and colleagues, who loaded them onto other computers. Infected programs were also

◀ *The Sasser worm infected the computers of hundreds of thousands of users in the middle of 2004. Infected computers continually turned on and off. Police discovered that the virus had been produced by a German high school student.*

downloaded from bulletin boards, which were early versions of Web sites. As computers were connected together by the Internet, viruses were spread more quickly, especially as e-mail attachments.

Triggers

Many viruses are triggered by a certain event. This may make their effects more spectacular, so people take more notice of them. (The programmers who produce viruses often want people to notice them, especially other programmers.) The trigger may be a time or date, or a specific command, such as saving or opening a file. The virus's attack may be a harmless message, or it could be very destructive, such as deleting all the files on the computer.

Worms and Trojan horses

There are two main types of computer viruses: worms and Trojan horses. A worm copies itself and spreads through the connections in a computer network. It infects other machines on the network and repeats the process. A copy of the worm scans the network for another computer that has a gap in its security. Worms make computers run more slowly, and information cannot travel between

computers as quickly because the worm takes up all the bandwidth—the size of the connections between the computers. Certain worms, such as the Sasser worm of 2004, spread so quickly that the Internet slowed down completely.

A Trojan horse is a virus hidden inside another program—similar to the Greek story of the Trojan horse. Trojan horses may allow other people, such as hackers, to take control of the computer or capture security information, such as passwords. Not all Trojan horses spread themselves. Instead, hackers target them at specific computers or networks. However, other Trojan horses will copy themselves by sending themselves to other computers by e-mail.

The Trojan horse is triggered when someone opens the program that is attached to the e-mail message. This program will generally claim to be a game or some other form of entertainment. Once loaded, however, it does something quite different.

Boot sector viruses

This early type of computer virus spreads by hiding itself in an invisible location on the hard drive. When the computer reads an infected disk, the virus is copied from the disk to the computer's memory. From there, it writes itself to the boot sector on the hard drive. The boot sector is an area of the hard drive that controls how a computer boots up, or starts. The virus is constantly reloaded and can copy itself onto other disks. Boot sector viruses are less common because computers now protect the boot sector.

E-mail viruses

An e-mail virus travels in e-mail messages. It copies itself by automatically mailing itself to people in the e-mail address book of the infected computer. It is designed just to copy itself and does not damage the computer directly. However, it can slow networks because so many e-mails are being sent.

In 2000, for example, the Love Bug virus sent messages to people with "ILOVEYOU" in the subject line. Anyone who opened the e-mail triggered the virus. The virus raided the e-mail addresses from the computer's address book and sent the same message to everyone listed there. However, it mixed up the addresses, so it appeared that the e-mails were being

> **DID YOU KNOW?**
>
> The Code Red worm replicated itself more than a quarter of a million times in about nine hours on July 19, 2001. Experts predicted that the worm would clog the Internet so completely that things would grind to a halt. The Code Red worm was designed to attack the White House web server in an attempt to overwhelm it. The U.S. government changed the address of the White House computer network to circumvent the attack and then issued a general warning about the worm to computer users worldwide.

sent by other people. The virus caused many problems across the world. A programmer in the Philippines was found to be responsible.

Hoaxes

Virus hoaxes can cause just as much trouble as a real virus. E-mails containing faked warnings are spread by concerned computer users. Although they contain no software, the e-mails are still being copied and spread, and they can clog up networks in the same way as real viruses.

Some hoax e-mails instruct unsuspecting computer users to delete certain files on their hard disk, saying they are viruses. However, these files are essential parts of the computer's software. When they are deleted, the user finds that his or her computer no longer works.

Virus protection

Antivirus software detects all but the latest viruses. Updates are issued every month to keep the system working. A typical virus scanner will check disks, e-mails, and Internet downloads for viruses on a computer. It then repairs infected files and isolates files that cannot be repaired. New viruses are sent to

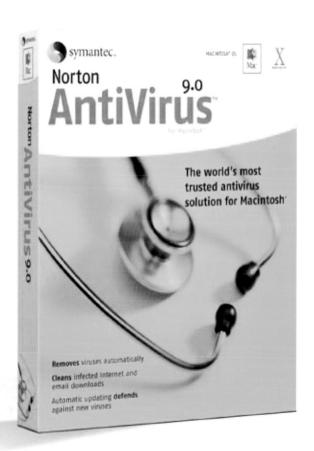

◄ *Antivirus software protects computers from attack by viruses. The software must be updated regularly so it can deal with the latest viruses.*

▲ *Computer viruses may be used during a military or terrorist attack on a country. A virus could destroy important communications systems and make it hard for commanders to respond to the attack. The U.S. Department of Defense, based in the Pentagon in Washington, D.C., has a special e-warfare unit that specializes in preventing the disruption of communications systems by viruses.*

researchers who figure out a way of stopping them. If the virus never appears again, researchers class the virus as dormant.

Viruses will always be a threat to computers, but there are several things that can be done to reduce their effects. Important data on the computer must be backed up regularly. An e-mail virus is not dangerous until the infected e-mail is opened. The best way to protect a machine is to never open unexpected e-mails and downloads from unreliable sources. Always delete mail from unknown sources.

People create computer viruses. They are usually people who spend a lot of time on their computers. Some of them want to prove that they are good programmers. Others want to show that they have the power to cause large-scale problems.

A virus author has to write the code, test it to make sure it spreads properly, and then release the virus. Although the Internet allows computer viruses to spread quickly, it also helps to catch the authors. Each computer connected to the Internet has an address, similar to a phone number. This is called an IP address, and every e-mail is marked with this information. Sophisticated virus authors may be able to cover their tracks to some degree, but there is always some way to detect them.

See also: COMPUTER • INTERNET • SOFTWARE • TELECOMMUNICATIONS

Viscosity

Which liquid pours more easily—a jug of water or a jug of syrup? The water, of course, flows more easily because the syrup has greater thickness, called viscosity, than the water. The higher the viscosity of a liquid, the more difficult it is to make the liquid flow.

There are two basic ways in which fluids (liquids and gases) flow: laminar flow and turbulent flow. In laminar flow, the fluid moves evenly. If syrup is poured very carefully, it comes out of the jug in a steady stream. The other type of flow—turbulent flow—occurs when the liquid reaches a certain velocity (speed in a given direction). Then the flow becomes less even. If an attempt is made to pour syrup very quickly, it starts to come out of the jug in uneven spurts.

The critical point at which laminar flow changes to turbulent flow is different for every fluid. It depends on the nature of the fluid. In particular, it depends on its viscosity.

What causes viscosity?

Viscosity is the property of fluids that causes them to resist flowing. All fluids have this property. The molecules of a fluid move against each other, which results in friction (the force set up by the molecules of the fluid rubbing together). It is this friction that causes the viscosity of the fluid, which may also be described as the fluid's thickness or thinness. The more the molecules interact with each other, the higher the viscosity. Heating a liquid reduces the friction between the molecules, so the liquid is less viscous than when it is cold. On the other hand, a gas is more viscous when it is hot than when it is cold.

Measuring viscosity

Scientists compare the viscosities of fluids using an instrument called a viscometer (also called a manometer). There are three types of viscometers.

The first type measures the flow of fluid through a vertical narrow glass tube. A widely used version is called the Ostwald viscometer. A fixed amount of fluid is passed through the tube. The time the fluid takes to flow through is a measure of the viscosity. Another instrument of this type is called the cup viscometer. This is a cup, with a small hole in its base, which is filled with liquid. The viscosity is measured by the time it takes for the liquid to drain through the hole.

▶ *Syrup forms coils as it is poured. Syrup is a highly concentrated sugar solution, and it is very viscous. If syrup is diluted with water, it becomes less viscous because its molecules move farther apart, causing less friction.*

The second type of viscometer measures the time taken for a heavy object to fall through a fixed distance of the fluid being measured. An example is a falling sphere viscometer, in which a ball bearing is dropped through a column of fluid.

The third type is the rotational viscometer. This instrument works on a principle known as viscous drag. If a rotating object is immersed in a fluid, the object will be slowed down in relation to the viscosity of the fluid. The cone-and-plate viscometer works in this way.

This type of drag also occurs if the fluid in its container is rotated around a stationary object immersed in the fluid. The object is hung from a spring, which is connected to a scale. The deflection of the object (the amount it moves) is measured on this scale. It is in proportion to the viscosity of the fluid. This method is useful because continuous measurements can be made over a long period.

The coefficient of viscosity

It is not always sufficient to compare the viscosities of fluids. Sometimes scientists require more precise information. They need to know a number called the coefficient of viscosity, which tells them the exact viscosity of a fluid. English mathematician and physicist Isaac Newton (1642–1727) first suggested a way of finding out this information.

The theory depends on the nature of laminar flow. A fluid with laminar flow moves in layers. The speed of each layer is different, but it relates to the layers above and below it. The difference in speed between adjacent layers is the velocity gradient. Newton figured out that if he knew the force within the fluid, the velocity gradient, and the surface area of the fluid, he could devise an equation that would give the coefficient of viscosity for any fluid.

◀ *Isaac Newton first proposed the theory that fluids flow in a series of layers. The rate at which adjacent layers flow relative to each other, and the force needed to do so, determines the fluid's viscosity.*

In 1850, a scientist named Stokes was studying objects falling through viscous fluids. Stokes found that the object first accelerates and then settles down to a steady speed, known as the terminal velocity. This speed is reached when the downward force of gravity acting on the object is equal to the force of the liquid's upward thrust and viscosity. So it is possible to calculate the coefficient of viscosity of a fluid from the terminal velocity of an object falling through it.

Importance of viscosity

The viscosity of a fluid is often very important in its applications. The viscosity of motor oil, for example, affects how well it can lubricate the parts of an automobile engine to make them run smoothly. It is necessary to measure the viscosity of a liquid at various temperatures when considering it for use as a lubricating oil. The temperature is important because the lower the temperature, the higher the viscosity. Lubricating oils used in airplanes must function at subzero temperatures. So their viscosity at these temperatures is critical.

Pitch is a tarlike substance used to waterproof boats, and it is extremely viscous. At standard room temperature and pressure, it appears solid. However, an ongoing experiment at Brisbane University, Australia, shows that a drop will slowly form and fall every seven or eight years.

See also: ATOM AND MOLECULE • LUBRICATION • NEWTON, ISAAC • PRESSURE

Vitamin

People need to eat a variety of different foods to stay healthy. Vitamins are some of the important elements that food and drink provide. Most vitamins cannot be made in the body, so they must come from food. People who do not get enough vitamins may develop potentially life-threatening deficiency diseases.

In the developed world, most people eat enough varied foods to provide a balanced diet. This diet ensures all the vitamins necessary to maintain good health. However, people in the developing world often do not have enough to eat, or have such a limited diet that they suffer from vitamin deficiencies, which can lead to serious diseases.

A constant supply of vitamins is essential for good health, but only tiny quantities are needed at a time. As can be seen in the box on page 1932, twelve different vitamins are found in various foods. People who do not eat a variety of foods may suffer from a particular type of deficiency.

Vitamin A

This vitamin is necessary for healthy eyes. Sufferers become unable to see in the dark. As the deficiency progresses, the surface of the eyes clouds over, and eventually the sufferer may become blind. Vitamin A is found in foods containing fat and can be made by the body from carrots and green vegetables. Undernourished people in any part of the world tend not to have enough fatty foods and often insufficient vegetables, so vitamin A deficiency is common wherever malnutrition (inadequate diet) is a widespread health problem.

B-complex vitamins

There are several B vitamins—cyanocobalamin, folic acid, niacin, pyridoxine, riboflavin, and thiamine—collectively known as the B-complex vitamins. They serve a variety of functions.

B1, or thiamine, is found in wheat and corn. It is also present in rice, but when the rice has been refined or processed to remove the brown outer covering, the vitamin is lost. In places such as

▼ Fresh fruit is full of vitamins A, C, E, and some B-complex vitamins. Nutritionists recommend that people eat between five and nine servings of fruit and vegetables every day to ensure that they get an adequate supply of vitamins and minerals.

◀ *In the 1960s, U.S. scientist Linus Pauling (1901– 1994) proposed the theory that very large doses of vitamin C could prevent infections, especially colds.*

Southeast Asia, where polished rice forms most of the diet, people often have a thiamine deficiency. This deficiency results in a disease called beriberi, which causes the legs and arms to swell and may affect the heart if it is not treated.

Shortage of another B vitamin, niacin, causes the disease known as pellagra. This disease occurs in people who eat little else but corn and is found frequently in Africa and in areas of India, South America, and Europe. Pellagra affects the skin, the digestive system, the mouth, and the brain.

Vitamin C

Perhaps the best-known vitamin is vitamin C, which can be obtained by eating fresh fruit and vegetables. People who do not have enough vitamin C develop a disease called scurvy, which results in bleeding, anemia, and damage to the bones and teeth. With a shortage of this vitamin, the body fails to repair itself properly. Anyone who smokes or drinks a lot of alcohol may need to take larger amounts of vitamin C than usual. It is important to note that vitamin C may be destroyed by too much processing or cooking.

Vitamin D

Unlike most other vitamins, vitamin D can be made by the human body—in skin exposed to sunlight. Vitamin D can also be obtained from various fatty foods such as milk, cheese, and liver. People who stay indoors too much may develop vitamin D deficiency, though a summer vacation can give the body enough stores of the vitamin to last a year. People with dark skin who live in countries without a great deal of sunlight may also lack sufficient vitamin D because the dark pigment in their skin has the effect of blocking out sunlight.

Vitamin E

One of the vitamins that is still not properly understood, despite a great deal of research, is vitamin E. It is found in many foods, particularly cereals, eggs, and nuts. It is believed to prevent problems of blood supply to the muscles and blindness in premature babies.

Vitamins to cure disease

Scientific investigations looking at the role of vitamins in the body have only been taking place since the twentieth century, and there is still much more to be learned. In the years between 1915 and 1945, scientists thought that they would find many different kinds of vitamins. They began naming them after letters of the alphabet but did not get beyond the letter K and discovered none that they could label F, G, or H.

Although these substances are grouped together under the term *vitamin,* they differ greatly in their chemical composition. Taking in too much of one vitamin can upset the balance of other vitamins in the body. Thus an overdose of any one vitamin (except, perhaps, vitamin C) may be as dangerous as a deficiency. Overdoses of vitamin A may cause fragile bones, loss of appetite, and enlargement of the liver and spleen. Too much vitamin D can lead to calcium deposits in the arteries and kidneys plus weight loss, vomiting, and headaches.

DID YOU KNOW?

The table below contains a list of all the vitamins people need to maintain good health. It also describes some of the deficiency diseases that can result if the diet does not contain enough vitamins. Most people in the developed world eat a balanced diet that provides all the necessary vitamins to keep the body working properly. Deficiency diseases are most common in the developing world, where people do not have access to a range of foods.

A (retinol) *Good sources:* Carrots, dairy products, eggs, fish, green vegetables (particularly spinach), liver, margarine
Deficiency symptoms: Blindness; lung aggravation; night blindness; rough, dry skin

B1 (thiamine) *Good sources:* Beans, breakfast cereals, flour, meat, milk, peas, potatoes, wheat germ, whole-grain cereals, yeast extract
Deficiency symptoms: Beriberi, digestive disturbances, fatigue, memory loss, loss of appetite, nervousness

B2 (riboflavin) *Good sources:* Eggs, green vegetables, milk, variety meats such as liver
Deficiency symptoms: Cracked corners of mouth, dizziness, eye fatigue, light sensitivity, poor digestion, slow growth, general sores

B6 (pyridoxine) *Good sources:* Bread, cereals, dairy products, eggs, liver, yeast
Deficiency symptoms: Fatigue and depression; low levels sometimes found in women who are pregnant or have a hormone problem

B12 (cyanocobalamin) *Good sources:* Dairy and animal products (particularly liver)
Deficiency symptoms: Degeneration of nerve cells, fatigue, memory loss, anemia

Folic acid *Good sources:* Bananas, bread, green vegetables, oranges, pulses, variety meats such as liver
Deficiency symptoms: Digestive disturbances, growth and sleep problems, anemia

Niacin *Good sources:* Bread, dairy products, eggs, fortified breakfast cereals, lean meat
Deficiency symptoms: Depression, headaches, memory loss, loss of appetite, nervous disorders, pellagra

Pantothenic acid and biotin
Good sources: Most foods
Deficiency symptoms: Very rare

C (ascorbic acid) *Good sources:* Fresh fruit (particularly kiwi fruits and citrus fruits such as lemons, limes, and oranges), potatoes, green vegetables
Deficiency symptoms: Anemia, bleeding gums and associated gum disease, scurvy

D (calciferol) *Good sources:* The most important source of vitamin D is from sunlight; food sources include butter, cod liver oil, egg yolk, fatty fish, margarine
Deficiency symptoms: Bone deformities such as rickets

E (tocopherol) *Good sources:* Most foods, particularly cereal products, eggs, nuts, vegetable oils, wheat germ
Deficiency symptoms: Anemia in premature infants

K (phylloquinone) *Good sources:* Vitamin K is made by bacteria in the intestines; associated food sources include dark green vegetables, liver
Deficiency symptoms: Problems with the blood-clotting process

◀ *Vitamin D is unusual in that its best source is from the action of sunlight on the skin.*

Nevertheless, many people believe that extra supplies of certain vitamins can prevent or cure particular illnesses. Apart from guarding against colds, vitamin C is thought to be effective in the treatment of certain cancers. Certainly, cancer treatments such as radiotherapy can cause a patient to need extra amounts of vitamins.

Extra vitamin A is given to some people who suffer from skin complaints such as psoriasis (in which new skin cells form before the old ones can be shed). Congenital ichthyosis is another disease that may be treated with vitamin A. This complaint has the effect of making the skin resemble fish scales because there are not enough sweat and oil glands. Drugs made from vitamin A may also be used to treat tumors.

Healthy children

Expectant mothers require excellent nutrition to cope with the demands of the growing fetus and the huge changes their bodies endure. In the final stages, pregnant women should consume an additional 200 calories a day; before then, it is solely the quality of the food they eat that is important because it is directly responsible for the growth of the fetus. Premature babies (who have spent less than nine months inside the mother) have less body fat than other infants. Body fat contains stores

▲ *Without enough vitamin D, children develop rickets, a disease that makes their bones grow deformed.*

of vitamins A, D, E, and K, so these children will need extra nourishment. If they are fed breast milk, vitamin supplies will soon be replenished.

Special deficiencies

Most people in the developed world have the opportunity to eat a balanced diet, but some are more prone to vitamin deficiencies. These include the elderly, who can have difficulty in looking after themselves, and the sick, whose illness destroys vitamin supplies. Alcoholics may drink a lot but eat little, so they may suffer from vitamin deficiencies.

See also: CARBOHYDRATE • FAT • METABOLISM • NUTRITION • PROTEIN

Voice analysis

Speech is one of the keys to the success of the human race. Speaking is a complex process, involving the brain, the tongue, and the vocal cords. Changing the shape of the face can also change the meaning of the spoken word. Studying the human voice helps scientists discover new ways to aid people who are unable to speak or hear properly.

The human voice is a sound produced in part of the throat called the larynx. The larynx contains soft flaps called vocal cords. Air blowing through the larynx makes the cords vibrate and produce a humming noise. Muscles pull on the vocal cords to make them tight or loose, and this changes the pitch of the humming sounds. Tight cords produce high-pitched sounds. Loose cords produce deep buzzing sounds.

The lips, teeth, and tongue can change the sounds produced by the vocal cords to form short sounds called syllables. The syllables are then merged together to form words. Most words contain just a few syllables, although longer words have many syllables.

The brain controls all the different body parts involved in speech. The sounds are then detected by the ears, and it is the brain again that recognizes each spoken word and figures out its meaning.

No other organism on Earth has a means of communication as complex and effective as that of a human. From the earliest times, the human voice has been used for identifying people, places, and things and for giving instructions. Spoken words are also a useful tool for describing past, present, and future events.

The way speech is controlled and then under-stood is being examined by scientists from many different fields of research.

▲ *English physicist Stephen Hawking (born 1942) cannot speak because he has a muscle-wasting disease. Instead, he inputs what he wants to say into a computer, which speaks for him.*

Voice identification

Everybody's voice is unique. The shape of the mouth and nose has an effect on the sounds they produce. Also, people are taught to pronounce words in slightly different ways.

Police investigators can use a recording of a voice to identify a criminal. The voice is converted into a complex graph called a speech spectrogram. The graph is a visual description of the spoken words, showing the variations in pitch and intensity in the individual's voice. Each speech spectrogram is different enough to identify a person's voice. Spectrograms are not as reliable fingerprinting, however, because the sound of the voice can be affected by other noises and air conditions. In addition, people can disguise their voices and even pretend to speak like someone else.

Conversation with computers

Speech spectrograms have also played an important part in developing synthesized speech—the voices that are produced by computers. By reproducing the pitch and intensity of human speech, some computers can give information verbally as well as on a display screen or printout. However, talking computers continue to sound stilted. There are so many different elements that go into making up human speech, it is difficult to reproduce it artificially with much success.

Computers can also recognize the spoken word. Voice recognition is an increasingly important part of computer software. For example, automated telephone systems are often able to recognize spoken words. A recorded voice asks a caller to answer a simple question, usually by saying "yes" or "no," or by saying a name. The computer then directs the call to the correct part of the system, where the caller can speak to a real person or answer more preprogrammed questions.

Many word-processing programs can recognize spoken words, so people can dictate their letters and other documents straight onto the screen without having to use a keyboard. Over time, the program learns to recognize a particular user's voice, so it makes fewer mistakes.

▼ *Computer software is now very good at recognizing the words people say as long as they speak clearly. In this picture, a user is controlling a computer with simple spoken instructions. More advanced voice-recognition software replaces the keyboard and types what a person says on the screen automatically.*

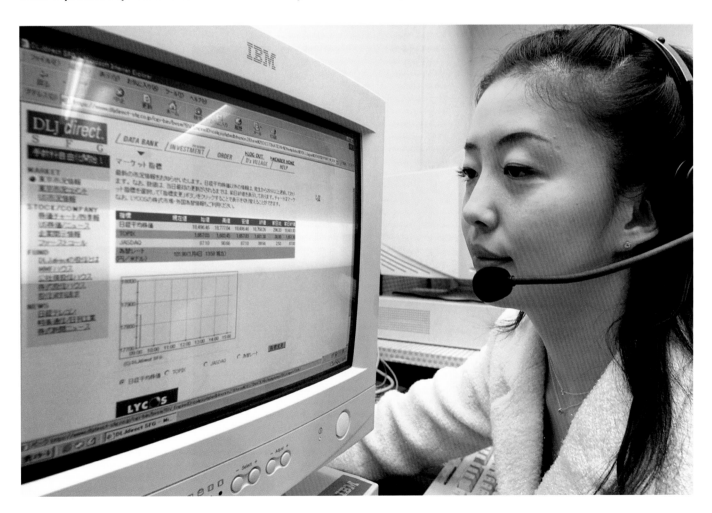

When words fail

Perhaps the most important use of voice analysis is to help people that are unable to speak. A person who specializes in solving this problem is known as a speech therapist or speech pathologist. The speech therapist studies the many different elements that go into the production and reception of speech and then determines why the system is not functioning and what to do about it.

Speech therapists most often work with children. First, they check how well the child can hear. If the child has poor hearing, he or she will not be able to learn how to make the correct sounds needed for speech. There may also be a problem with the vocal cords and the palate (roof of the mouth). The strength of the tongue and facial muscles, the structure of the nose and sinuses (spaces behind the face), and the healthy state of the nerves and the speech centers in the brain are also things that may affect a person's ability to speak properly. Emotions can play a part in speech problems as well.

DID YOU KNOW?

The human brain is the ultimate in voice-recognition computers. It can decode and interpret the sounds that make up a one-syllable word even before the last letter has been spoken.

The electrical activity of the brain, including the parts concerned with speaking and understanding language, can be detected using a device called an electroencephalogram (EEG). The electrical signal from the EEG is displayed as a moving graph on a computer screen. Comparing the brain activity of the patient with that of a person without speech problems can reveal brain damage that affects speech, hearing, or the ability to understand words.

Hearing problems are measured with a machine known as an audiometer. The audiometer broadcasts words or tones at different volumes, and the patient

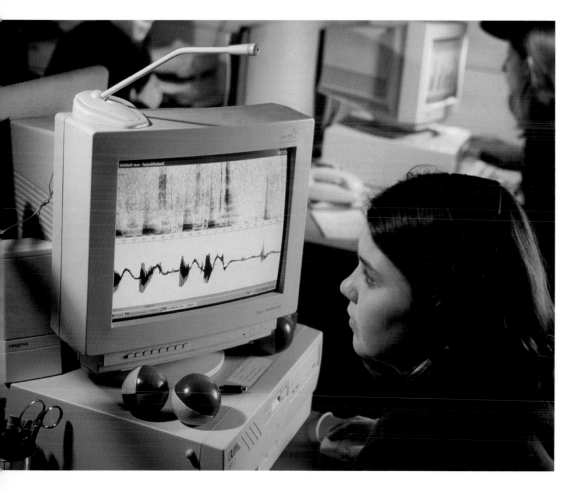

◄ This speech therapist is studying the different parts of a person's voice using computer software. The speech is displayed as a pattern on the computer monitor.

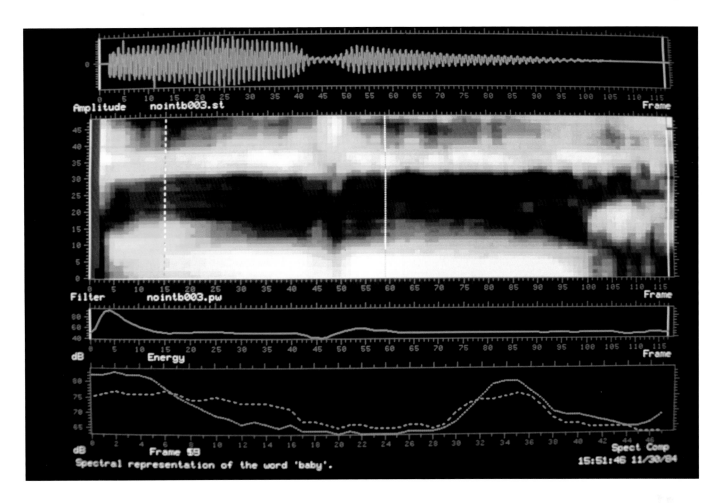

Amplitude   nointb003.st

Filter   nointb003.pw

dB   Energy

dB   Frame 59

Spectral representation of the word 'baby'.   15:51:46 11/30/84

▲ *This picture shows the different ways of measuring the word* baby *produced by a speech synthesizer.*

must press a button when he or she hears a sound. The use of the audiometer helps build a picture of what a person can or cannot hear.

Treating speech problems

Stuttering (stammering) is a common speech problem. It often appears in children at age six or seven. There are several causes, including physical and emotional problems. A number of methods have been developed to treat the condition.

Most stutterers get stuck on the beginnings of words and can only repeat these sounds. Rhythm can be improved by using a metronome, which is a timing device usually used by musicians to keep in time with the music.

Another cause of stutterering is thought to be the way in which people hear their own voice—known as feedback. (A person hears his or her own voice

differently from everyone else because the sound echoes inside his or her head.) A device that resembles a stethoscope can block out any unwanted feedback and prevent stuttering.

If the brain is damaged, the ability to speak might be lost. The brain can no longer process the information correctly, and sufferers might be unable to remember the names of things, omit words from sentences or put words in the wrong order, or repeat fixed words and phrases.

Speech difficulties prevent people from communicating, particularly if their brain damage also prevents them from writing. Sufferers may type messages on computers, as this is easier than writing with a pen. Computers can even detect the movements of a person's eye. So somebody who cannot move at all can still write messages by just looking at a screen.

See also: BRAIN • EAR AND HEARING • SPEECH

Volcano

Great damage can be caused by volcanoes. These openings in Earth's crust helped create the atmosphere and the oceans by releasing gases and water vapor from Earth's interior. Soils formed from volcanic rocks are usually good for growing crops.

▲ *The explosion of Mount St. Helens in 1980 blew away most of the north side of the volcano. A new lava dome is growing in the crater, and small emissions of gas and ash show that the volcano is still active.*

Volcanoes are vents (holes) in Earth's crust. They are created when molten material, called magma, is forced upward from Earth's interior to the surface. Magma consists of molten rock, called lava, and volcanic gases, including water vapor. The temperature of magma is around 2000 to 2190°F (1093 to 1199°C). Near the surface, the gases may separate from the lava. The lava then emerges in broad streams, which burn and bury everything in their path until they finally cool and harden.

Flowing lava has spread over large areas, such as the plateaus of the Columbia and Snake river basins in Washington and Oregon. In these regions, lava covered an area of about 116,000 square miles (300,000 square kilometers). Some individual lava flows were about 120 miles (195 kilometers) long. Basalt is the most common rock formed from flowing lava.

Sometimes, the gases remain in the magma. They expand and shatter the magma into fragments, called pyroclasts, which are thrown into the air. Pyroclasts include fine material such as volcanic dust and ash. Some fragments, called lapilli, are pebble-sized, while others are as large or larger than a loaf of bread. The large fragments are called volcanic bombs.

Much magma never reaches Earth's surface. Enormous bodies of magma that have cooled and hardened underground, often beneath mountain ranges, are called batholiths. Smaller bodies, called laccoliths, often arch up to form a dome over the underlying rocks. Sheets of magma injected into rocks parallel to existing layers are called sills. Sheets of magma that cut across existing layers are called dikes.

Active and extinct volcanoes

Active volcanoes are those that have erupted in recent history. Of the world's five hundred or so active volcanoes, only about 20 to 30 are in eruption at any one time—although a few, such as those in Hawaii, are in almost continuous eruption. In most volcanoes, eruptions do not last long. During the periods between eruptions, the volcanoes are said to be dormant (inactive). Periods of dormancy may last for thousands of years. Volcanoes that have not erupted in recent history and that are considered unlikely to erupt in the future are said to be extinct.

Mount St. Helens in Washington state had been dormant for 123 years before its spectacular eruption on May 18, 1980. The northern flanks of the mountain were blown away, which released a glowing avalanche of hot, volcanic dust and rocks

12 miles (19 kilometers) deep and 5 miles (8 kilometers) wide. After the eruption, lahars (mud flows)—formed from shattered rock and melted ice, snow, and water—flowed down the mountain. Geologists have estimated that lahars have caused more destruction of property and killed more people than any other kind of volcanic activity in recent times.

composite volcano

cinder cone

shield volcano

fissure volcano

◄ *Several different types of volcanoes exist, ranging from tall, steep-sided cinder cones to fissure eruptions that do not form mounds but release fluid lava that can cover a wide area.*

Volcanoes are often classified according to the way in which they erupt. Some erupt explosively. Others erupt by releasing massive amounts of fluid lava but without major explosions. These are said to be quiet volcanoes. Other volcanoes are intermediate in type.

Explosive volcanoes

Volcanoes explode when hot gases are trapped in thick, pasty magma. The gases expand and break up the magma, throwing fragments into the air. Explosive volcanoes usually form steep-sided and cone-shaped mountains. The larger, heavier fragments fall near the vent, piling up into a high heap, while smaller pieces are thrown farther away.

Violent explosions can destroy much of a volcanic mountain. The biggest volcanic explosion occurred on the Greek island of Thera (formerly Santorini) in the Aegean Sea. This explosion took place around 1470 BCE and caused the collapse of much of the original island, removing an estimated 15 cubic miles (62.5 cubic kilometers) of rock. After the explosion, a caldera (crater) was created in the seabed. It covered 31 square miles (80 square kilometers). This great eruption may have led to the legend of the lost continent of Atlantis.

The most powerful volcanic explosion in modern times took place in 1883 on the Indonesian island of Krakatoa, between Sumatra and Java. The explosion was heard 2,900 miles (nearly 4,700 kilometers) away. Krakatoa was uninhabited, but the explosion generated huge tsunamis that hit the coasts of Java and Sumatra, drowning more than 36,000 people. Large rafts of pumice—a light rock formed from frothy lava—spread over nearby seas. The Krakatoa eruption was estimated to have the force of 26 atomic bombs, yet this was only one-fifth of the estimated power of the Thera explosion.

An unusual kind of explosive eruption creates what is called a *nuée ardente* (glowing cloud). A famous example occurred in Martinique, where the

volcano Mount Pelée began to erupt in April 1902. Volcanic ash spread over large areas, and poisonous gases killed many animals in the nearby town of St. Pierre. However, the full force of the volcano was not felt until May 8, when a dark cloud of ash and hot gases emerged from the vent and rolled down the mountainside. It destroyed St. Pierre and killed around 30,000 people.

Quiet volcanoes

The lava that pours out of quiet volcanoes is usually flowing and contains comparatively little gas. As a result, explosive eruptions do not occur. However, visitors to Hawaii will testify that quiet volcanoes can put on a great display, shooting fountains of blazing lava up to 1,600 feet (488 meters) into the air. Side vents, also called satellite or parasitic cones, often form when the magma finds new outlets through the sides of a volcano. One quiet volcano, Mount Etna in Sicily, has about two hundred of these satellite cones.

The speed at which lava flows depends on how liquid it is. One type of lava common in Hawaii is called *pahoehoe*. This lava is extremely fluid and may travel great distances at up to 12½ miles (20 kilometers) per hour, sometimes reaching the sea. When *pahoehoe* hardens, it often looks like a rope made of satin, covered by a continuous skin. Another kind of lava also has a Hawaiian name—*aa* (pronounced "ah-ah"). *Aa* hardens into uneven blocks with rough, jagged surfaces.

◀ *Lava that is very fluid can travel for many miles before it begins to cool and harden. Thicker lavas contain more gas and are usually thrown into the air in fragments, hardening and falling as ash or pumice.*

Because quiet volcanoes release flowing lava, they are usually flat in profile. Geologists often call them shield volcanoes. Their gentle slopes are usually only between two and ten degrees. The world's largest volcano, Mauna Loa on Hawaii, is a shield volcano.

Intermediate volcanoes

Most volcanoes are intermediate in type. As such, they may erupt explosively, although most eruptions are accompanied by lava flows. Vulcano, the

DID YOU KNOW?

Volcanic ash consists of tiny particles that are less than ⅕ inch (0.5 centimeters) across. Small plants and animals buried by falling volcanic ash are usually very well preserved as fossils.

volcano in the Italian Aeolian Islands from which the word *volcano* is derived, is intermediate in type. Vesuvius, to the north, is another intermediate volcano. Lava flows have occurred during most of its eruptions since the huge explosion in 79 CE, including the most recent eruption in 1944, when lava buried the town of San Sebastiano. Most intermediate volcanoes are composite. In this type of volcano, layers of ash and other shattered fragments alternate with layers of lava.

Why volcanoes occur

Of the world's main landmasses, only Australia has no volcanoes. However, the distribution of volcanoes is irregular. Most lie near or on the edges of the plates into which Earth's crust is divided. Along the oceanic ridges where plates are moving apart, for example, molten magma wells up to fill the gaps and form new crustal rock. The magma is probably created by a radioactive heat source beneath the crust. Underwater volcanoes on these ridges release magma that cools rapidly to form pillow lava, which is coated with a glassy skin. Continued eruptions of lava pile up to form underwater volcanic mountains. Some of these may rise above the water and become new islands. An example is Surtsey, which is a volcanic island that appeared off the coast of Iceland in 1963.

Other volcanoes lie close to what are called subduction zones, where the edge of one plate is being pushed downward beneath another. As the plate descends, parts of it and the overlying continental crust are melted, creating magma. Some of this magma rises through cracks in the crust and reaches the surface in volcanoes such as Mount St. Helens. The volcanoes of Indonesia also lie near subduction zones.

A few volcanoes lie far from the oceanic ridges and subduction zones. These volcanoes are fed with magma that has probably been created by an isolated radioactive "hot spot." As the plate moves over this hot spot, magma breaks through from time to time and forms volcanoes. Eventually, an island formed by one of these volcanoes moves past the hot spot, and the volcano becomes extinct. In this way, a chain of volcanic islands is created, but active volcanoes occur only on the last island in the chain.

Predicting eruptions

Unexpected eruptions may cause much damage. As a result, scientists have been studying ways of predicting eruptions. Observation stations have been built around many active volcanoes in populated areas. Scientists at these stations keep careful watch on changes in temperature and pressure inside the volcano, and they check for Earth tremors.

Instruments called tiltmeters are used to record changes in slopes caused by rising magma. The electrical and magnetic properties of rocks are also affected by heat, so changes in these properties are other guides. Another factor is the composition and temperature of gases venting from fumaroles (small holes). Despite much research, however, the prediction of when eruptions will occur and how powerful they might be is still not very accurate.

◀ *Scientists monitoring active volcanoes sometimes need to get very close to lava flows to collect samples. They wear protective suits that reflect the heat of the lava away from their bodies to keep them cool.*

See also: EARTHQUAKE • MOUNTAIN • PLATE TECTONICS • ROCK • TSUNAMI

Volta, Alessandro

Italian physicist Alessandro Volta was one of the first scientists involved in the study of electricity. He is best remembered for inventing the battery. Volta also invented the electrophorus and the electroscope and studied the behavior of heat and gases.

Volta was born in 1745 into a poor but noble family in Como, Italy. At the age of 18, he became interested in physics and chemistry. This interest led Volta to many discoveries and inventions. In recognition of his contribution to the study of electricity, the volt is named in his honor. A volt is a unit used to measure the force pushing an electrical current through a wire.

Volta hoped to develop laws of electricity, much as English scientist Isaac Newton (1642–1727) had developed the laws of motion. This led Volta to invent several devices that could store electrical charges and then measure them. He was interested

▼ *Volta showed his battery to French emperor Napoleon Bonaparte in 1801. Napoleon was impressed with Volta's invention and awarded the scientist several honors and a pension.*

in other areas as well. In 1776, he discovered methane gas (CH_4). This is "natural gas" that is used as a fuel in houses and power plants.

In 1775, Volta invented the electrophorus. This was a simple device that produced static electricity. Static electricity does not form an electrical current. Instead, it accumulates on objects as electrical charges.

Soon, Volta became a professor at the University of Pavia. There he invented the electroscope, which was a device to measure electrical charges.

Inventing the battery

After learning that Italian physicist Luigi Galvani (1737–1798) had made electrical currents flow through the muscles of a frog, Volta began to study new ways of making electricity. He saw how touching different metals produced electrical current. The current worked best with wet metals. Volta made the current stronger by using many pieces of metal at once. He made a pile of disks, alternating between copper and zinc. This "voltaic pile" was the first battery.

Electricity is a flow of particles called electrons. Although Volta did not understand this, the pile produced electricity because electrons were moving from one disc to another down the column.

◄ *This picture shows a replica of Volta's pile—the first electric battery. Volta made the first voltaic pile in 1799, using a column of copper and zinc disks. An electrical current flowed from disk to disk.*

See also: BATTERY • ELECTRICITY

V/STOL aircraft

The vertical or short takeoff and landing (V/STOL) aircraft resembles a conventional airplane and can fly in the same way. Unlike a conventional airplane, however, it can lift itself straight off the ground without using a long runway. It can also land by hovering and descending vertically in the same way as a helicopter.

▲ *This convertiplane transport aircraft has four propeller engines that can rotate so they face upward as well as forward. With the engines pointing up, the convertiplane can take off in the same way as a helicopter. When it is airborne, the pilot can rotate the engines forward and fly the convertiplane in the same way as an airplane.*

In the 1950s, aircraft designers began to search for a way to combine the advantages of a helicopter with those of a conventional fixed-wing airplane. They wanted an aircraft that could rise into the air and land without a runway, hover in the air, and also fly at higher speeds and carry heavier loads than a helicopter.

Problems with helicopters

Helicopters do not need a runway to land; they can use any open area. They can also hover in one place for long periods. This ability makes them extremely useful for jobs such as rescuing sailors from sinking ships and stranded climbers from mountaintops. However, they cannot fly very fast and are unable to carry large loads. Few helicopters can fly more than 250 miles (400 kilometers) per hour. Most can only reach half this speed.

New helicopter designs with added propellers and wings were not successful. Engineers then tried to redesign the airplane to give it some of the main advantages of the helicopter, such as being able to hover and not needing a long runway to land.

The helicopter-airplane

Initially, engineers designed a helicopter-airplane, called a convertiplane. The simplest form has the body and tail of a conventional airplane but slightly shorter wings. On the tips of the wings are rotors, which are winglike blades that rotate around a central point. Helicopters use rotors to fly instead of wings. The rotors of a convertiplane can be swiveled so they face upward (similar to the rotors of a helicopter), or they can face forward (similar to the propeller engine of a conventional airplane). When they face upward, the rotors lift the aircraft vertically into the air. When they face forward, the rotors push the aircraft forward. During takeoff, the convertiplane's engines are positioned in the same way as the engines of a helicopter. When in the air, the engines are used like those of an airplane.

Many convertiplanes were designed, but only a few were ever made in large numbers. Some worked by moving each rotor and keeping the wings flat; others were designed so that the entire wing rotated.

Using jet power

Convertiplanes could carry heavier loads, but they were not able to fly much faster than conventional helicopters. To reach higher speeds, jet-powered V/STOL (vertical or short takeoff and landing) aircraft were developed. Although both airlines and air forces were eager to have such aircraft, few of the designs ever went into mass production because there were just too many difficulties to be overcome. However, the design of one British company, Hawker Siddeley, was a success. After

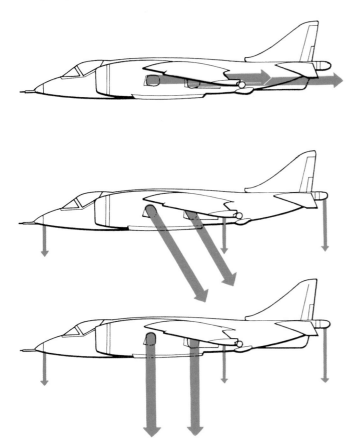

failing with its design for a 400-seater transport V/STOL, Siddeley developed a small fighter aircraft called the Hawker Harrier.

This fighter used vectored thrust. Jet engines work by blasting hot gases through a nozzle at the rear of the engine. These gases produce a force that pushes the aircraft along. In normal jet engines, the thrust is always directed backward. The Harrier's two engines also direct the thrust backward to push the aircraft forward. However, they can also direct the gases downward, so the thrust pushes the airplane upward for takeoff. Each engine does this by having two exhaust nozzles that can be rotated to point in both directions.

The AV-8

The AV-8 is the U.S. Marine Corps version of the British Hawker Harrier. It uses Rolls-Royce Pegasus jet engines—similar to the vectored-thrust engine used in the Harrier. This engine is a turbofan, with a large propeller-like wheel at the front that draws in more air and produces more thrust. All modern airliners use turbofans, while most fighters use turbojets, which are more powerful but less efficient. Because turbofans use a spinning fan, they cannot be made to fly faster than the speed of sound; AV-8s are therefore slow compared to many fighter aircraft.

▲ *From bottom to top, these three illustrations show how the AV-8's nozzles are positioned, from the vertical takeoff to forward flight. Smaller compressed-air jets, called puffers, keep the aircraft balanced when it is hovering.*

▶ *The AV-8 is very useful for landing on aircraft carriers and even smaller warships.*

Proved in battle

The AV-8 and the Harrier resemble conventional fixed-wing fighters. Their main role is to attack targets on the ground, while supporting ground troops. The Harrier was first used in action by the British in the Falkland Islands conflict of 1982. Harrier pilots shot down 22 enemy airplanes without losing a single aircraft. Since then, the V/STOL fighter has proven to be just as effective during other conflicts.

Vertical landing is very useful with the AV-8, especially in bad weather. Many airplanes have to carry extra fuel in case they cannot land at one airfield and have to find another. This V/STOL aircraft can fly slowly to a landing spot, hover until its position is exactly right, and then land. Even the heaving decks of aircraft carriers in a rough sea are no problem. During the Falkland Islands conflict, Royal Navy Sea Harriers landed on aircraft carriers in the rough South Atlantic while the decks were moving up and down by about 16 feet (5 meters).

Quicker maneuvering

What makes the AV-8 so deadly in combat is the way in which its engines can be used to change thrust direction while in flight. By altering the direction of their exhaust nozzles, pilots can jump out of the way of a much faster aircraft. They can also change direction more quickly and pull out of dives more sharply than most other fighter aircraft.

The AV-8 is designed for conventional (not nuclear) warfare only. It is used in front-line situations, for defending troop positions and attacking an enemy, and it cannot carry weapons of mass destruction. The U.S. Marines consider it an ideal plane for commando-type operations.

The AV-8A is equipped with a wide variety of weapons that can weigh up to 5 tons (4.9 tonnes), although its usual weight is 2.5 tons (2.5 tonnes). It can carry air-to-air missiles, rockets, and bombs.

The AV-8B is a newer version of the same fighter. It can carry more weapons and fly farther than the AV-8A. While the AV-8A is made of metal, the wings of AV-8B are made from a composite of carbon fibers and hard resins. This material is lighter but stronger than metal. The AV-8B is thus more efficient, flying longer with less fuel. The extra strength also makes it even more maneuverable.

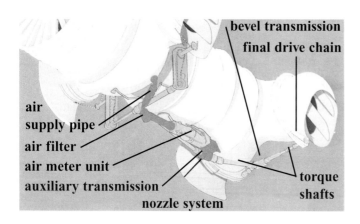

bevel transmission
final drive chain
air supply pipe
air filter
air meter unit
auxiliary transmission
nozzle system
torque shafts

▲ *The four nozzles are linked to a control lever operated by the pilot in the cockpit.*

Future fighter

The AV-8s used by the U.S. Marines and the Harriers and Sea Harriers used by the armed forces of Britain and other countries are due to be replaced by a new design of V/STOL fighter.

The F-35 Joint Strike Fighter is being developed by Lockheed Martin. This fighter will be the most advanced warplane ever made when it comes into service, sometime around 2010. Most of the F-35s that will enter service will not be V/STOL aircraft. However, one version of the fighter will be, and the approach used to achieve V/STOL capabilities is quite different from that of other designs.

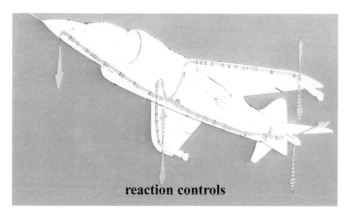

reaction controls

▲ *When hovering or moving at low speeds, the reaction control system uses air from the engine to keep the aircraft stable.*

◄ *This experimental V/STOL aircraft was tested by the Bell Aircraft Corporation in 1957. The aircraft had tiltable rotors on its wingtips.*

Similar to the AV-8 and Harrier, the F-35's single rear engine has vectored thrust—it can be made to point downward. Because the engine is at the back of the aircraft, any downward thrust it produces would make the fighter cartwheel out of control, rather than rise upward. To balance the thrust from the engine, the V/STOL F-35 uses a large fan just behind the cockpit.

When the aircraft is flying normally, this fan is covered. When the plane is hovering, or moving up or down, flaps in the fighter's upper and lower surfaces open to expose the fan. The fan blade rotates around, sucking air from above through the aircraft and pushing it out underneath. This creates enough thrust to balance the force produced by the jet engine at the back.

The F-35 uses a turbojet engine, so it is supersonic—it can fly faster than the speed of sound. However, the space taken up by the fan means that the V/STOL version cannot carry as much fuel and cannot fly as far as other models.

The V/STOL for passenger service

One day it might be possible to use the technology developed for the AV-8 and Harrier and F-35 to make passenger aircraft that can fly from airports no larger than a parking lot. However, while military V/STOL aircraft can take off by rising straight up when they need to, this is only done when absolutely necessary. When it takes off vertically, an aircraft can carry only half its maximum load. However, using just a short runway for takeoff allows the plane to carry a full load.

Another problem with V/STOL aircraft is that they exhaust a lot of hot and unburned fuel from their engines. A person has to stand at least 32 feet (10 meters) away from a plane the size of an AV-8 during landing or takeoff. Larger, passenger-carrying V/STOL aircraft would probably have even more dangerous jet exhausts. In addition, the noise from V/STOL airliners might be too much for populated areas of large cities.

No passenger V/STOL aircraft have ever been put into service, and research into this new kind of aircraft continues. However, many smaller airports close to residential areas use STOL (short takeoff or landing) airliners and cargo planes. STOL aircraft need only a short runway, which is much easier to locate in crowded and expensive cities.

See also: AERODYNAMICS • AIRPLANE • AIRPORT

Wankel engine

A conventional gasoline engine has pistons that are driven up and down by combusting (burning) a mixture of gasoline and air. In a Wankel, or rotary, engine, the pistons are driven in a circular motion by combustion. This motion is much more efficient than other internal combustion engines.

Gasoline engines are driven by repeated small explosions produced by the combustion of a compressed mixture of gasoline and air. In a conventional gasoline engine, these explosions force a piston down inside a cylinder. The piston then returns to the top of the cylinder, compressing more fuel-air mixture for combustion. The reciprocating (up-and-down) movement of the piston is changed to a rotary (turning) movement by connecting rods and a crankshaft, and this rotary movement is transmitted (passed on) through a gearbox and driveshafts to the wheels of the vehicle.

In a rotary engine, the combustion of compressed gasoline and air drives a rotary piston in a circular motion. Therefore, there are no connecting rods, no complex crankshaft, and fewer moving parts.

Wankel's rotary engine

The rotary combustion engine was invented by German engineer Felix Wankel (1902–1988) in 1927. Rotary engines are therefore also known as Wankel engines. Wankel's rotary engine design uses a rotary piston, called a rotor, shaped like a rounded triangle. This rotor revolves inside an outer chamber shaped like a fat figure-eight. This shape is carefully calculated to provide the rotor with the right movement. The rotor has a circular hole in its center, with gear teeth facing inward. As the rotor rotates, the gear teeth drive a circular, stationary crankshaft inside.

The three "points" of the triangular rotor each have a seal. These seals maintain constant contact with the walls of the outer chamber as the rotor turns, creating three spaces into which the fuel-air mixture is drawn, compressed, and combusted, before the burned gases are finally exhausted.

How a rotary engine works

Because each side of a rotor acts like the piston in a reciprocating combustion engine, it is only necessary to look at the movement of one side of a rotor to see how a rotary engine works.

Suppose that the front seal on one side of a rotor has just passed the inlet port in the outer chamber. As the rotor turns, the gap between the side of the rotor and the chamber wall gets bigger, drawing in fuel-air mixture. The rear seal on that side of the rotor then passes the inlet port, sealing off the space.

The rotor continues to turn, reducing the space between the side of the rotor and the chamber wall, thus compressing the fuel-air mixture. When the

◀ *The inventor of the rotary combustion engine, Felix Wankel, displays one of the later versions of his innovative engine.*

space is at its smallest, a spark plug fires, igniting the mixture and causing it to explode. This explosion turns the rotor, thereby also turning the crankshaft inside it.

Finally, the front seal on this side of the rotor passes the exhaust port. The gap between the rotor side and the chamber wall again gets smaller, pushing the burned gases out through the port. The cycle then repeats itself.

As there are three sides to a rotor, fuel-air mixture is ignited three times during each complete turn of a rotor. However, because of the gearing, the crankshaft inside a rotor turns three times as fast as the rotor. Therefore, there is one explosion and power stroke for each rotation of the crankshaft.

Advantages of rotary engines

Rotary engines have a number of advantages over reciprocating engines. Significantly, compared to an equivalent reciprocating engine of the most common, four-stroke type, a rotary engine produces more power. Each combustion event in a rotary engine lasts through 90 degrees of the rotor's rotation. Because the crankshaft rotates three times for each turn of the rotor, each combustion event lasts through 270 degrees of the crankshaft's rotation. This means that a single-rotor engine delivers power for three-quarters of each revolution of the output shaft. A single-cylinder four-stroke engine, on the other hand, delivers power for only one-quarter of each revolution of the crankshaft.

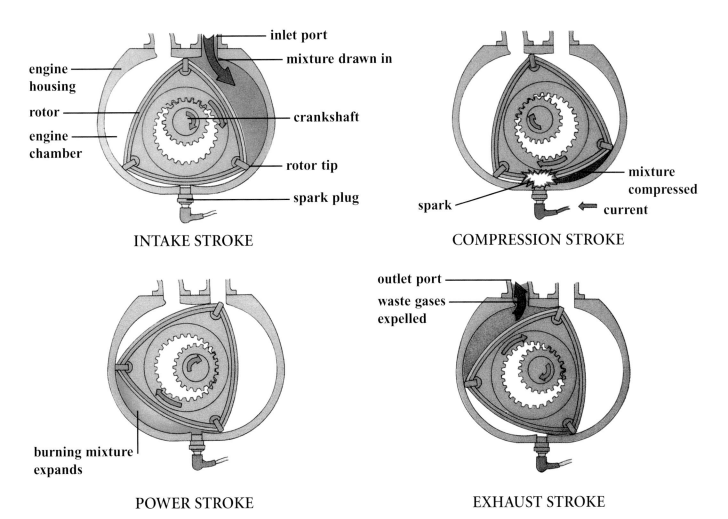

INTAKE STROKE

COMPRESSION STROKE

POWER STROKE

EXHAUST STROKE

▲ *Rotary engines use a triangular rotor that revolves off-center around a stationary crankshaft gear. Air-fuel mixture is sucked in through an inlet each time one side of the rotor passes it. The engine housing is shaped so that the mixture is compressed as the rotor moves. A spark then ignites the mixture, which turns the rotor and forces out waste gases during the exhaust stroke.*

Rotary engines also run smoothly compared to reciprocating engines. The violent, up-and-down motion of the pistons in reciprocating engines creates a lot of vibration. This vibration is not only undesirable, it also wastes power.

Another advantage of rotary engines is that they are mechanically simple. They have only two basic moving parts—the rotor and the crankshaft. Because there are none of the connecting rods, pistons, camshafts, and valve gears that are found in reciprocating engines, less power is wasted, and there is less chance of wear and tear damaging the engine. This increases performance and reliability.

Due to their lack of moving parts, rotary engines are also comparatively small and light. Their small size makes them easier to package. Rotary engines can often be mounted centrally in an automobile, which improves the vehicle's handling. The light weight of rotary engines also gives them a better power-to-weight ratio than a reciprocating engine, thus improving the vehicle's performance.

Problems with rotary engines

Despite the many advantages of rotary engines over more conventional engines, they have suffered from some problems that have served to limit their widespread adoption.

In early models, the rotor seals (also called rotor tips) often quickly wore out, causing some cases of engine damage. The problem was solved by developing alloys with which to make the seals and by spraying the surface of the engine chamber with a coating that was then ground to a smooth finish. Unfortunately, this early problem caused a lasting doubt about the reliability of rotary engines.

Also, rotary engines do not burn fuel as efficiently as four-stroke gasoline engines. Although great improvements have been made with recent rotary engines, such as Mazda's Renesis, they still cannot match the economy of the latest four-stroke engines. For this reason, the application of rotary engines has remained limited, largely to sports cars, for which fuel economy is of less concern.

▲ *This Mazda RX-8 sports car is unique in being the only mass-produced automobile to be built with a rotary engine in recent years. The manufacturer is at the forefront of improving rotary engine design.*

See also: AUTOMOBILE • DIESEL ENGINE • INTERNAL COMBUSTION ENGINE

Warplane

Warplanes are military airplanes specially designed for combat. Different warplanes are designed to do different things. Some carry bombs or missiles to attack targets on the ground. Others attack and shoot down enemy warplanes. Many modern warplanes are expected to do all of these things and more.

Five years after the Wright Brothers made their first flight at Kitty Hawk, North Carolina, in 1903, the United States became the first country to adopt the airplane for military use. In 1908, the U.S. Army began to test planes for use in general observation. By flying over enemy positions, the pilot or observer could note the location of important targets invisible to an observer on the ground. By 1911, the first aerial bombing raid had been carried out by Italians against Turkish troops during their invasion of Libya. Hand grenades were dropped from an observation airplane onto an enemy camp below, causing more surprise than damage.

Observation

When World War I (1914–1918) broke out in Europe, most of the nations involved used airplanes for observation and reconnaissance. At the beginning of the war, planes were used almost entirely for artillery observation. This meant locating enemy positions, reporting the estimated ranges (distances) to the artillery gunners, and telling them if their shelling was accurate or not. These airplanes were generally known as scouts, and normally they carried the pilot and one observer passenger. Throughout the conflict, scouting remained probably the most important task performed by airplanes.

Because information gathering by this new method was very successful, both sides began to look for ways to prevent the enemy's scouts from "spotting" (observing) over their own lines. The airplane usually flew out of range of ground fire, which was easy before the development of anti-aircraft guns. On occasion, opposing scout pilots would confront each other in the sky, but they could not do much more than shake their fists at each other and perhaps shoot a few pistol or rifle rounds from a long distance away.

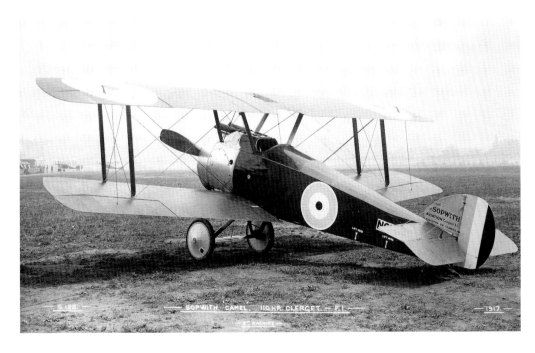

◄ *This Sopwith F1 Camel single-seat fighting scout dates from World War I. Slow and only lightly armed with twin machine guns, the Camel was typical of a number of aircraft that began the evolution of the specialized fighter aircraft.*

Shooting

Soon these warplanes had machine guns that could be operated by the observer from the rear cockpit, which was some defense against attack from behind. However, a breakthrough came in 1915 when French pilot Roland Garros (1888–1918) devised a way to shoot down an enemy plane in front of his airplane. Instead of attaching the machine gun to the rear cockpit—where it could only be fired above and behind—he fixed it to the fuselage (body) of his plane so that it faced directly forward through the arc of the propeller. All he had to do was point his airplane at an enemy plane and pull the trigger.

To prevent the bullets from damaging the wooden blades of his own propeller, Garros attached metal deflector blades to them so that any rounds that failed to pass between the blades would bounce off harmlessly. He quickly shot down five German airplanes, but one day his engine stalled over enemy lines, and he had to make a forced landing. Garros and his machine were captured, and the secret was out.

The Germans were impressed, so they decided to copy Garros's idea. They also made a major improvement. The Germans built a mechanical link between the machine gun and the engine that

▲ The P-51 Mustang was a successful American fighter aircraft from World War II. Most aircraft of this time were driven by propellers, but the development of the jet engine by the end of the war revolutionized the design and capabilities of warplanes.

prevented the gun from firing whenever a propeller blade was in the way. This interrupter gear was incorporated into their new Fokker E1 aircraft.

This airplane was the first true fighter, and it dominated the skies over France until the Allies developed an improved version of their own. In this way, scouts became fighters, and many legends were born in the early days of aerial dogfighting.

Bombers

Just as the fighter became a distinct aircraft type, so too did the bomber. At first, pilots and observers simply tossed an occasional grenade or iron spike onto the trenches below. This caused some small-scale damage; however, it was quickly recognized that if a scout plane could observe enemy positions, it could also drop explosives onto them.

Gradually, bigger and better bombs were developed, and with them larger and more powerful airplanes. When World War I ended in November 1918, easily maneuverable fighter planes could fly at speeds of 130 miles (210 kilometers) per hour or more, and twin-engined night bombers carrying crews of three or four could deliver several thousand pounds (thousands of kilograms) of bombs over enemy positions.

Design improvements

Improvements in the design and manufacture of military airplanes continued in the industrial nations until the start of World War II (1939–1945). By that time, the fighter had evolved from a wood and fabric biplane to an all-metal monoplane with a closed cockpit, armor plating to protect the pilot, and increased firepower. The latest machines could fly at speeds of more than 350 miles (565 kilometers) per hour, more than twice the speed of their World War I counterparts.

By the time of the Battle of Britain in 1940, when British Hurricane and Spitfire fighters fought off a massed German air attack, the warplane had become recognized by most countries as a major factor in the ability of a nation to defend itself and win a war. After World War I, many military planners believed that any future war could be won simply by bombing an enemy's civilian population until they surrendered. Most nations started rushing bombers into production. In fact, as the German Blitz on London in 1940–1941, and the later massed Allied raids on Germany, showed, civilians could be very resilient under air attack. They also showed that bombers were vulnerable to attack by fast and well-armed fighters.

DID YOU KNOW?

In addition to trying to make increasingly faster aircraft, fighter-plane designers also look to achieve high maneuverability. The more maneuverable a fighter, the easier it is for a pilot to avoid being engaged by enemy aircraft and hostile fire. One recent experimental U.S. aircraft was the X-29. It has an unusual forward-swept wing that gives the impression that the aircraft is flying backward. However, this radical configuration makes the aircraft very agile—perhaps too agile for the usual combination of a pilot and computer control system. It is feared that during some sharp turns at high speed, pilots in the X-29 may be subject to G-forces powerful enough to kill them.

Jet planes

The most significant advance in military aviation during World War II was the jet engine. The first jet plane to fly was the German Heinkel 178 in 1939. However, it was only in 1944, near the end of the war, that jet warplanes were ready for combat. The German Luftwaffe (air force) flew more than 100 operational Messerschmitt Me262 twin-jet fighters against Allied planes over Germany with great success in the last months of the war. Both the United States and Britain had developed their own jet planes during the war, but these saw no combat in the air before the war ended.

The Korean War (1950–1953) saw the first all-jet combat, between Soviet-built MiG and U.S. North American Sabre fighters in 1950. By the end of the 1950s, the piston-engined airplane was obsolete in combat roles, and many countries operated supersonic fighters—jet airplanes capable of flying faster than the speed of sound. Strategic jet

◀ *The intercontinental-range B-52 bomber was designed for the Cold War between the East and West from 1947 to 1991. The B-52 can fly at altitudes above 50,000 feet (15,240 meters) and can hit several targets hundreds of miles apart during one mission.*

◀ *One of the most versatile warplanes ever made is the Harrier, developed in Britain in the 1970s. The Harrier can take off and land from very short runways, or even vertically. Because it does not require a long runway, the Harrier can operate in many environments that would be inaccessible to conventional fighters. It is particularly suitable for operation from aircraft carriers. The Harrier's high level of control also makes it a maneuverable fighter.*

bombers were also developed that were capable of dropping nuclear or conventional bombs of devastating power. Now, however, strategic bombers are largely being replaced by the various types of long and intermediate range missiles.

As the postwar generation of jet fighters got faster, the design began to change to compensate for the effects of flight at close to and above the speed of sound. Wings and tails were swept back, and wings began to be anhedral (drooping downward) instead of dihedral (rising upward) to improve stability at high speed.

Computer and electronic technology

Perhaps the most significant advance in military aviation has been the rapid development of computer technology and electronics in the planning, design, and actual operation of modern sophisticated warplanes. Because a modern warplane carries so much elaborate technical equipment, it is far more expensive to produce than the warplanes of World War II.

To keep these costs as low as possible without producing less effective airplanes, most national air forces have concentrated on developing the multirole combat aircraft (MRCA). As the name suggests, an MRCA is an all-purpose airplane that can perform a variety of different military tasks. A modern multirole combat airplane, such as the Panavia Tornado or the Boeing/Northrop F/A-18, can be used for training, fighter interception, bombing, ground attack, or reconnaissance. Depending on the avionics (aviation-electronics equipment) carried onboard, and on how they are programmed, along with the weapons system carried, most modern MRCAs can perform any one of these tasks.

In addition to being adaptable, modern warplanes are also efficient. The Northrop Grumman B-2 bomber carries more bombs farther than the famous Boeing B-17 Flying Fortress bombers of World War II, but it can also fly up to five times as fast and is far better protected against attack.

▼ *Not all warplanes are supersonic fighters and bombers. Many, such as the giant Hercules transport aircraft in this picture, have other important roles.*

DID YOU KNOW?

The official world airplane speed record is Mach 6.72 (4,435 miles or 7,137 kilometers per hour), set by an X-15-2A over Edwards Air Force Base, California, on October 3, 1967. However, newer military aircraft may be capable of higher speeds and new records may since have been established in secret.

Avionics have also largely replaced the machine guns and cannons of World War II with highly accurate and very destructive guided missiles. These can be fired by one airplane against another plane that the pilot may not even be able to see. Most modern missiles are either radar guided or heat seeking, which means they steer toward an enemy airplane's jet exhaust. To protect against these missile attacks, most warplanes now carry electronic countermeasures (ECMs). These are

▲ *This B-2 Stealth Bomber and two F-117 Nighthawk stealth fighters have been designed to be invisible to radar systems. This gives them a significant tactical advantage because the aircraft can reach their target without detection. Even if these planes are detected, it is difficult for missiles to seek and destroy them.*

electronic systems designed to warn the crew of enemy attack and to throw the enemy missiles or planes off the plane's track.

Electronics have also played an important part in the development of all-weather airplanes since World War II. In those days, if the weather was bad, either the planes were grounded, or they were forced to fly over or around the area of bad weather. If the target was covered by cloud or fog, accurate bombing became impossible. In modern war-planes, complex and sensitive computerized radar guidance and Global Positioning Systems (GPS) act as the crew's "eyes," allowing them to concentrate on planning and executing their mission. Meanwhile, the airplane flies under the control of a computer, often at night, in bad weather conditions, or at very low altitudes to avoid detection by enemy ground radar.

The next generation

Amazing composite materials that can twist and bend in flight to suit a plane's maneuvers have allowed the design of fighter planes that would otherwise be impossible. One was the experimental X-29, whose radical forward-swept wings made it unstable but highly maneuverable. Compact high-speed onboard computers constantly adjust wing and tail surfaces to keep the plane on course. The U.S. Air Force has also developed top-secret stealth airplanes to be almost invisible to radar. They are shaped to scatter radar waves, coated with radar-absorbing materials, and to carry instruments that send the wrong images to enemy radar screens.

An advanced tactical fighter, called the F-22 Raptor, is also entering service. Computer-controlled devices in its composite wings will adjust the wing's many control surfaces for best performance at different speeds. It will have a cruising speed of Mach 1.5 over long distances and will also have radar-resisting features of stealth planes.

See *also:* AIRPLANE • HELICOPTER • JET ENGINE

Warship

A century ago, some warships still had sails. They were designed to fight large fleet battles using cannons at close range. Modern warships are built to fight in small groups, often using long-range missiles and torpedos. The crews may never see their enemy.

Up to World War I (1914–1918), naval battles were fought between large fleets. The Battle of Jutland, fought between the German and British navies in the North Sea in 1916, was probably the last great naval battle in the old tradition. Each navy had several large ships, heavily armed and massively armored, which steamed in lines. These ships had smaller, faster ships around them to keep the enemy's smaller ships from attacking the larger vessels. Tens of thousands of sailors took part.

Jutland was a victory for neither side, and the Germans started to think of other ways of fighting a war at sea. They were already having great success against British merchant ships with their submarines and with small groups of fast, powerfully armed ships. By the start of World War II (1939–1945), the German navy had a large number of submarines and some pocket battleships—lightly armored battleships that relied on speed to avoid fighting a group of enemy ships. Their guns were big enough to make them dangerous against even the largest British battleships, which had heavy armor plating and were slower than the German ships.

Aircraft against ships

During World War II, airplanes began to play an important part in naval warfare. The British Royal Air Force (RAF) could guard huge areas of sea much more easily than could a fleet of ships. RAF bombers destroyed German ships that were at anchor. German and Italian bombers and dive bombers almost prevented the British from supplying food and arms to the island of Malta.

▼ *This photograph of USS* Iowa *shows her firing all her big guns in a full broadside. Because of changes in naval warfare, battleships are now obsolete. USS* Iowa *was decommissioned by the U.S. navy in 1990.*

Torpedo bombers were more dangerous to large ships than ever before, in spite of quicker, more accurate anti-aircraft fire. Enough airplanes could swamp the defenses of a fleet. This was clearly shown at Pearl Harbor (December 7, 1941), where the Japanese bombed the U.S. Pacific fleet as it lay at anchor, and in the later sea battles in the Pacific. These battles were between fleets of ships, but, in fact, they were fought largely by aircraft from carriers.

It is the combined threat of warplanes and submarines against surface ships that has changed sea warfare during the last 60 years and altered the kinds of ships in the world's navies.

Types of warships

All warships are a compromise. The traditional battleship—with its thick armor plating, heavy guns, and huge size—was slow. A faster ship, such as a pocket battleship or cruiser, had to sacrifice some of its armor. If a really fast ship was required, it would need to have almost no armor at all—only light guns and torpedoes.

A naval battle was supposed to be fought by sending faster ships to catch the enemy's battleships, trying to damage them enough so that chasing battleships could overtake them. Airplanes were used to disable large ships, so aircraft carriers were developed from which they could be deployed. Carriers were very vulnerable to air attack themselves, so anti-aircraft ships were built to protect them. If an invasion was planned, the army would have to be placed ashore in landing craft, launched from assault ships.

Many of these different types of ships are no longer needed. Battleships, for example, have now entirely disappeared. They were useful only occasionally for their heavy armament.

Aircraft carriers are still in service, but they are only used for older types of airplanes. Vertical or Short Takeoff and Landing (V/STOL) planes, such as the Harrier, can land and take off from a small platform mounted on the deck of almost any warship, as can helicopters.

Of course, if a large number of planes must be concentrated in one place, the carrier is the answer. However, if an aircraft carrier is sunk by a submarine or airborne missile, all the aircraft on board will be lost, too. It may be better to spread the planes over a number of smaller ships to avoid losing them all at once.

The modern warship

Ships have changed because weapons have changed. The enormous guns have disappeared. Some traditional guns remain—mostly quite small, but accurate and effective. The main weapon now is the missile. There are types of missiles for all purposes: anti-aircraft (surface-to-air, called SAM), antisubmarine (AS), and antiship. As a result, many ships now look the same, differing only in their purpose and the missiles they carry.

The three main missile-carrying ships are the frigate, cruiser, and the guided missile destroyer. Other types, apart from the aircraft carrier, are assault ships, minesweepers, corvettes, and submarines. There are also many different types of fleet auxiliary vessels, which are the backup ships that carry and supply stores, ammunition, and fuel to the fighting ships.

Frigates

The modern frigate is the workhorse of the navy. It can take on any specialist role, or it can combine all the specialties in one general-purpose ship.

Frigates are small. Most are about 300 feet (90 meters) long with a displacement of 5,000 tons (4,500 tonnes). Many frigates have antisubmarine torpedo tubes and a helicopter, also with torpedos. Some ships have a Harpoon antiship missile launcher or Sea Wolf antimissile system. To give a steady platform for the weaponry and electronics, the ships must be stabilized.

▼ *This photograph shows the tender USS Emory S. Land in Souda Bay, Greece, with a minesweeper moored alongside receiving stores. Auxiliary vessels such as tenders are vital for maintaining a navy's capabilities.*

Some models of frigates, such as the British Type 22, are larger—485 feet (148 meters) in length, with a displacement of 5,300 tons (4,800 tonnes). They carry only one 4½-inch gun, unlike the ships of World War II, but they also have two 20-mm anti-aircraft guns, a Sea Wolf antimissile system, and quadruple Harpoon missile launchers. A helicopter can be used for ferrying supplies or as the "eyes" of the ship. The Type 22 has two gas turbine engines, giving a speed of 31 knots.

Even heavy armor plating is no defense against modern antiship missiles such as Exocets and Harpoons. In any case, armor above the waterline means that more weight must be carried below it as ballast (stabilizing counterweight). Without this, there is a risk of the ship capsizing. Therefore, most ships are now made as light as possible to give a higher speed for the same engine power. Often aluminum is used for the hull. Plates of aluminum are welded together over a framework designed to give stiffness and to resist underwater explosions. The framework is also carefully designed to be the minimum weight for the required strength.

Inside, the ship is divided into a number of separate watertight compartments so that if one is damaged and flooded, the rest of the ship is safe. Inside, too, weight is reduced as much as possible. Unfortunately, much of the radar, weapons guidance, and other electronic equipment must be as high above the waterline as possible so that they

◀ *The nuclear-powered aircraft carrier USS* **Nimitz** *enters Pearl Harbor, Hawaii. Nuclear-powered ships have a greater fuel range than conventionally powered vessels. Consequently, they can stay at sea for extended periods without having to refuel.*

can "see" the maximum distance. This equipment is heavy, so the mast must be sturdy to carry it all. The result is that much extra weight has to be put where it is least wanted—high above the waterline.

Some naval architects are beginning to think that a steel hull, which will have more weight below the waterline, might be better than an aluminum hull after all. Others believe that a completely new shape of hull, broader and not so deep, is the only answer.

Guided missile destroyers

Guided missile destroyers are larger than frigates. Their main job is to defend the more vulnerable ships, such as carriers and assault ships, from surface and air attacks. Guided missile destroyers are not as fast as frigates because they have the same engines in a larger hull. However, they are formidably armed, with advanced missile systems and radar. They also have an automatic-firing, 4½-inch gun, and they use helicopters as torpedo and missile launchers.

Aircraft carriers

Carriers are the last of the really large ships still in useful service. They date from the early days of flying in World War I. The first carriers had to have a long flat deck so that planes could increase their speed enough to become airborne. Until the arrival of the jet engine at the end of World War II, the carrier had

to change course and steer into the wind to provide extra speed for a plane taking off. Given the short length of the flight deck on aircraft carriers, this can still be a useful operation even now.

The flight deck is not long enough for a plane that is landing to be able to stop before reaching the end. So the pilot lowers a hook called an arrester hook, which catches one of a number of arrester wires stretched across the deck. The wire is not fixed tightly, which would stop the plane with a jerk. Its ends are held by a mechanism that absorbs the force of the plane gradually, slowing it down without damage.

Since the end of World War II, carriers have been developed to their peak. The steam catapult, used to help launch planes into the air, and the angled flight deck were both introduced by the British Royal Navy. The angled deck allows much more room for aircraft landing and taking off. Once a plane is safely down, it can quickly be moved out of the way, either to near the bridge or right forward.

Another Royal Navy innovation was the "ski jump," used to help launch V/STOL jets into the air. This is a ramp that extends over the bows that gives extra lift to Navy Sea Harriers at takeoff.

Elevators bring planes up to the flat flight deck from the hangars where they are stored and maintained. These hangars have a great deal of fire prevention equipment in case of accidents or any dangerous damage.

Assault ships

Troops may need to be taken by sea to fight in another country. It is not always possible to cross a land frontier, and rough ground may rule out an airborne landing. So most navies have assault ships, built to take troops and their equipment to a landing point from the sea.

Landing craft are small boats designed to carry troops, tanks, and light artillery a short distance away from a ship lying offshore. They were first used in World War II to recapture Pacific islands from the Japanese and to invade the mainland of Europe. The troops and their equipment sailed in conventional ships and were put over the side into their landing craft to go ashore.

Now the landing craft are carried in specially designed assault ships with the troops and their equipment. During the voyage, the landing craft are carried in a dry dock in the stern (rear) of the ship. When the time comes to deploy the troops, the ship fills ballast tanks in the stern with seawater. This lowers the stern in the water, flooding the dry dock so the landing craft can float out.

> ### DID YOU KNOW?
>
> Commissioned in 1961, USS *Long Beach* was the first nuclear-powered surface warship. Also commissioned that year was USS *Enterprise*, the first nuclear-powered aircraft carrier. It is also the largest warship ever built, at 1,123 feet (342 meters) long and weighing in at 99,000 tons (90,000 tonnes).

For some types of operations, landing craft may be replaced by hovercraft, which are much quicker. However, hovercraft cannot sail in rough seas, and a hovercraft's performance is severely reduced if its skirt has been damaged. For operations such as this, the V22 Osprey has been developed for the U.S. Marines. This is a tilt-rotor aircraft, a cross between an aircraft and a helicopter.

▼ *Guided missile cruisers, such as the USS **Gettysburg**, are relatively small and fast and can fire on targets from a range far exceeding that of even the largest guns. Because of this, they have now replaced battleships.*

◄ *This picture shows the high-tech bridge aboard the U.S. Navy's Littoral Surface Craft-Experimental (LSC(X)) Sea Fighter (FSF 1). Sea Fighter is a high-speed aluminum catamaran and is being used to evaluate the performance and mission flexibility of high-speed vessels for naval use.*

Mine countermeasures vessels

Like most other weapons, mines have become highly developed since the primitive explosive devices used during World War I. Modern mines are advanced electronic weapons that can lie underwater for years without harming ships. At any moment, they can be armed by a remote signal—and they are then deadly to any ship coming near.

Mine countermeasures vessels are therefore essential to any navy. These ships do not try to clear every mine that has been laid. Their job is to clear a safe shipping channel into a port that has been blocked by enemy mines. They have equipment to deal with any of the various kinds of mines that they are likely to meet.

Contact mines (which explode on contact with a ship's hull) are anchored to the seabed by a wire cable. The minesweeper cuts the cable using a paravane (a small, unpiloted craft towed by the minesweeper). The mine comes to the surface and can be exploded safely.

Magnetic mines, first used by the Germans during World War II, explode when a metal ship draws close to them. The mine detects the magnetic field of the ship and detonates the explosive. To avoid setting off magnetic mines, the hull of a minesweeper and as much of the structure and fittings as possible, must be made of a nonmagnetic material. Many Royal Navy minesweepers, for example, are built of glass-reinforced plastic (GRP). Magnetic mines are exploded by pulses of electricity carried in a long cable towed by the minesweeper.

Acoustic mines are detonated by the sound of a ship's propeller in the water. Various types of sound generators are used to explode them. New mechanisms for mines are always being developed, and minesweepers need methods and devices to deal with them.

Latest trends in warship design

One modern missile can destroy a warship in a few minutes. Keeping the missile from hitting the ship is easier, cheaper, and quicker than building warships that cannot be destroyed. So ships are now equipped with advanced devices that can locate and destroy missiles moving at high speed only a few yards above the sea.

Many modern ship designs also make use of "stealth" technology, as used in some aircraft. By carefully designing the surface shapes and angles of a ship's hull and superstructure (the bridge and other parts above the main deck), it can scatter any radar waves hitting it, rather than directly reflecting them. This makes the ship less easy to find and track with radar.

A recent idea is to build warships from a set of modules (standard parts). Whichever guns are needed can be slotted into the hull size that suits the navy concerned. This makes ships quicker to design and build and therefore cheaper.

See also: AMPHIBIOUS VEHICLE • GUN • MISSILE AND TORPEDO • SHIP AND SHIPBUILDING

Washing machine

Before there were laundromats in every town and washing machines in many homes, washing clothes was time-consuming and laborious. Items had to be washed by hand, and stained clothes had to be scrubbed hard. Wet laundry was also heavy and took a long time to dry.

Modern automatic washing machines make doing the laundry quick and easy, and people do not think twice about washing their clothes several times a week. Before the washing machine was invented, however, cleaning clothes was a tough job. People did not have washing powders or liquids for cleaning out dirt, so they had to soak their dirty clothes in streams or boil them in water to get the dirt out of the them. Stubborn stains had to be scrubbed out by hand with a brush or by beating the clothes with a rock. Washing took a long time and a lot of effort. As a result, people did not do their laundry often, perhaps once a week, but generally less frequently. Instead, people kept wearing their clothes even when they were dirty and smelly by modern standards.

Help at hand

The first washing machine was invented by English furniture maker Henry Sidgier. The design was surprisingly similar to that of a modern machine, although it was powered by hand instead of an electric motor. Sidgier's machine consisted of a six-

▼ *Washing machines are now common household appliances. Clothes are put into smaller machines through a door on the side, while larger models are loaded through a door on the top of the machine.*

sided wooden tub. A handle on the side of the tub was attached to a wooden cage fitted inside. Clothes were loaded into the cage, and then the tub was filled with water and soap. Turning the handle moved the clothes in the cage through the water. Water rushing through clothes pushed the dirt out of them. This is exactly the same process used by modern washing machines.

The soap and other laundry products loosened the dirt stuck to the material, which made it easier for the fast-moving water to wash the dirt away.

Once the clothes were clean, the water was emptied out of the tub, and clean water was added to rinse the soap out of the clothes.

Early washing machines were also fitted with wringers, devices used to dry the clothes. Wringers used a number of rollers to squeeze the water out of wet clothes. Clothes were passed between the rollers by turning a handle on the wringer. After being wrung out, the clean clothes dried more quickly.

Automated washing

By the early twentieth century, washing machines were powered by electric motors, but they all used the same method to clean clothes. Even today, there are still two basic designs of washing machines—agitator machines and tumbler machines.

Agitators move the clothes using a central cone, fitted with fins, that spins around inside the tub. The fins on the cone push the clothes through the water. Agitator machines are loaded through a lid at the top. Tumbler machines are loaded through a door in the side of the machine. The whole tub, including the clothes, are spun around so the water and clothes tumble over each other.

Instead of using a wringer, modern machines force the water out of cleaned clothes by spinning the tub rapidly. This makes the water in the clothes fly outward through small holes in the tub wall. The clothes stay inside the tub and gradually get dryer. Washer-drier machines heat the clothes so the water in them becomes steam. This steam is then sucked out of the tub. Most modern washing machines are controlled by computers. People can choose the temperature of the water, the size of the load, and the length of wash, rinse, and spin cycles.

◄ *This early electric washing machine was made by a company in Canada in the 1920s. Its design is similar to hand-powered machines, but an electric motor under the wooden tub was used to churn the laundry inside. The laundry was then squeezed dry with the wringer, which was also driven by the motor.*

See also: COTTON • DYE AND DYEING • FIBER • TEXTILE • WOOL

Water

The colorless liquid called water is familiar to everyone. It has no smell and little taste. Water is the most common substance on Earth and covers 70 percent of the planet's surface. Water is present in all plants and animals, and without it life could not exist.

Plants and animals all contain large amounts of water. It is essential to many of the biological and chemical reactions that allow life to exist. Water also has many industrial uses.

Properties of water

Water is so common in nature that for many years people thought it was an element (a single substance). In the eighteenth century, scientists discovered that it was a compound made up of two elements, hydrogen and oxygen. Each water molecule (the particles of which it is composed) contains one oxygen atom and two hydrogen atoms. So the chemical formula of water is H_2O. Although water is a simple compound, the arrangement of its molecules in the liquid and solid states is complex and results in some unusual properties.

Water exists in three physical states—solid, liquid, and gas—that depend on how closely the molecules are packed and how fast they are moving. Water molecules are attracted to each other by a process called hydrogen bonding, in which the hydrogen atoms of one molecule are attracted to electrons in the oxygen atom of a neighboring water molecule. The molecules are closest together when the water is a liquid, so they tend to stay in this form longer. If heat is added or taken away, the liquid will change into steam or ice.

▶ *People need to drink around 4 pints (2 liters) of water every day to hydrate the body and keep cool. Water is also needed to carry substances around the body as solutions of blood, plasma, or urine.*

Adding heat makes the water molecules move so fast that they can overcome the attractive forces of hydrogen bonding and move apart. Water boils at 212°F (100°C), at which point it turns into water vapor (steam). This is a much higher temperature than the boiling point of other compounds with molecules of a similar size.

Hydrogen bonding is also the explanation for the unusual behavior of water when it freezes at 32°F (0°C). Most liquids contract (decrease in volume) when they freeze, but water expands. When heat is taken out of liquid water, the molecules move more slowly, and the electrical attraction is able to hold them farther apart in a fixed structure. An ice cube takes up more space than the water that was frozen to make it, which is why frozen water pipes sometimes burst. Liquid water is more dense (the molecules are closer together) than ice, so an ice cube will float in a glass of water rather than sink.

Solubility

The shape of a water molecule and its electrical properties are what make it such a remarkable compound. Instead of sitting on either side of the oxygen atom, the hydrogen atoms are both on one

◀ *Much of the world's freshwater takes the form of ice in glaciers. Glaciers look blue because the weight of the ice pushes out any air molecules that may have been trapped between snowflakes when they fell.*

DID YOU KNOW?

Water is vital because all living things need it. More than half the human body is made up of water—if the water were removed, the body would simply be a pile of salts.

side of the oxygen atom. This V-shaped arrangement makes water electrically positive at the hydrogen end and negative at the oxygen end of the molecule. When the charges are unevenly balanced like this, the molecule is called a polar compound.

The polarity of water molecules gives water the ability to dissolve many other substances. If crystals of common salt (sodium chloride; NaCl) are stirred into water, the electrical charge of the water molecules helps to pull the sodium and chlorine atoms apart. The water molecules then surround the sodium and chlorine, preventing them from recombining. The salt is said to be "in solution." In fact, water does not occur in a pure state in nature but usually has minerals and gases dissolved in it.

Most of the water in the world is in the form of seawater, which covers about 70 percent of Earth's surface. Seawater tastes salty because of the large quantity of sodium chloride that it contains. There are 35 pounds (16 kilograms) of salt in every 1,000 pounds (455 kilograms) of seawater. Freshwater is not pure either. Rain contains dissolved gases and small mineral crystals. When it falls to Earth, the water seeps into the soil before joining the rivers and reservoirs. As it travels through the soil, other substances dissolve in the water.

Hard water is the result of rainwater containing carbon dioxide (CO_2) running over limestone (calcium carbonate; $CaCO_3$). It dissolves the limestone to form calcium and magnesium salts. When the water evaporates, the salts are deposited again, sometimes in the form of crystals. The same process occurs when hard water is boiled in a kettle. The "fur" that builds up inside the kettle is calcium bicarbonate $Ca(HCO_3)_2$.

The presence of calcium and magnesium salts in water can be a nuisance—it is difficult to get a good lather with soap and hard water. In areas with hard water, a softening process may be introduced. Softening involves swapping the calcium and magnesium ions for more soluble sodium ions.

See also: RAIN AND RAINFALL • WATER CYCLE

Water cycle

The water cycle describes how water moves through the environment. Most of Earth's water is in the ocean. This evaporates into the air and then falls onto the land as precipitation, which soaks into the ground and flows into streams and rivers. Eventually, the water ends up back in the ocean.

▲ Waterfalls are a visible part of the water cycle. They show water flowing downhill, under the force of gravity, on its way to the ocean.

The study of Earth's supply of water is called hydrology, and scientists often call the water cycle the hydrological cycle. The energy that keeps the cycle going comes from the heat of the Sun.

Around 70 percent of Earth's surface is covered by water. The oceans contain about 328 million cubic miles (1,370 million cubic kilometers) of water, which is more than 97 percent of the world's total water supply. Of the other 3 percent, three-quarters makes up the ice of Antarctica and the Arctic region. The remaining water is found in rivers, lakes, and groundwater (soaked into rocks underground), or in the air as water vapor.

How much water is needed?

The minimum amount of freshwater required to sustain human life is small—only about 36 cubic feet (1 cubic meter) of drinking water per person per year. However, people use water for other purposes besides survival. The average person uses 1,000 cubic feet (28 cubic meters) a year, but the demand varies from place to place. In industrial cities, the average person uses 6,500 cubic feet (181 cubic meters) a year. A person living in a rural area of a developing country limits water use to 70 cubic feet (2 cubic meters) every year. However, the amount of water used for drinking, cooking, and washing is small compared to that used by farms and factories. In the United States, for example, half of all the water used is consumed by factories. Most of the rest is sprayed on crops to help them grow.

The origins of the water cycle

The water cycle starts when the Sun's heat evaporates pure water from the surface of the oceans. The salt in the seawater is left behind. Because the oceans are so large, the amount of water evaporated is enormous. It totals about 120,000 cubic miles (500,000 cubic kilometers) of liquid water every year.

As the water evaporates, the liquid turns into a gas called water vapor. Because the air above the ocean is being warmed, it rises upward, carrying the water vapor with it. As the air rises, it cools. As the vapor in the air cools, it begins to turn back into a liquid. This liquid forms tiny droplets around specks of dust that are being blown in the wind. These water droplets form clouds. As the air continues to cool, more and more liquid water fills the cloud. Eventually, the cloud cannot hold any more liquid, and the water falls down to the ground as precipitation (rain, hail, sleet, or snow). Precipitation is pulled down by the force of gravity. This force is an important part of the water cycle.

Perhaps 90 percent of the water evaporated from the oceans falls back into the sea as precipitation. However, some of the water vapor is blown over the continents. As it cools, this vapor forms clouds and then falls as precipitation on the land. Every year, 9,600 cubic miles (40,000 cubic kilometers) of freshwater fall on dry land.

Some of the precipitation never reaches the ground because it is reevaporated in warmer air nearer the ground. Also, much of the precipitation that does reach the surface is quickly evaporated by the heat of the Sun. However, most of this water will fall on land somewhere else, probably as rain. In certain conditions, clouds form snow, hail, or mist instead of rain.

Ice and running water

Some precipitation arrives on land as snow. In polar lands and high mountains, the snow becomes squeezed into ice. This ice, called a glacier, flows slowly downhill under the force of gravity.

Some glaciers and ice sheets reach the sea. There, chunks of ice break away to form icebergs. The icebergs float away and gradually melt. The water has returned to the ocean, and the water cycle starts again. However, other glaciers end in mountain regions where they melt and form a lake or

▼ *This illustration shows the distribution of water on Earth (measured in cubic kilometers). The freshwater that falls onto land each year is only a tiny part of the world's water supply.*

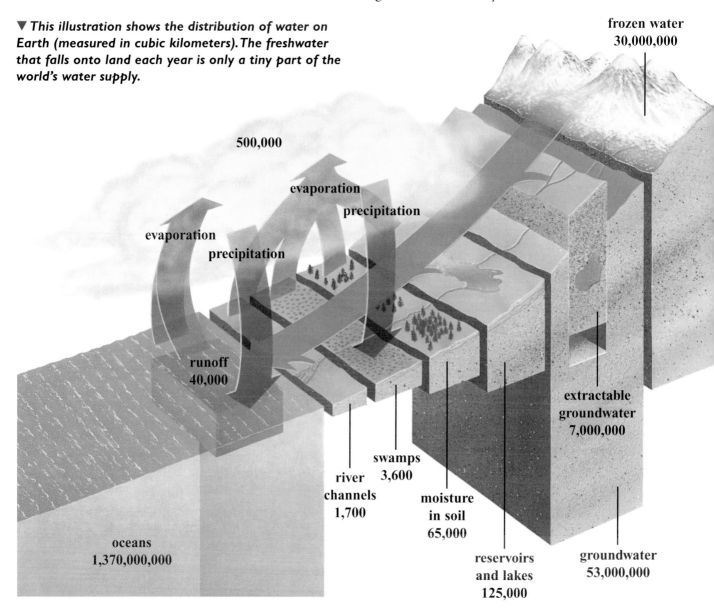

frozen water
30,000,000

500,000

evaporation

precipitation

evaporation

precipitation

runoff
40,000

extractable
groundwater
7,000,000

swamps
3,600

river
channels
1,700

moisture
in soil
65,000

oceans
1,370,000,000

reservoirs
and lakes
125,000

groundwater
53,000,000

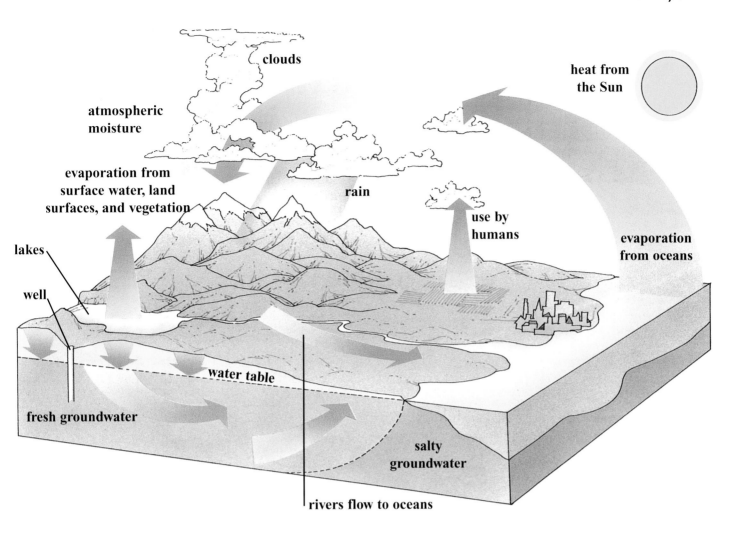

clouds

**heat from
the Sun**

**atmospheric
moisture**

**evaporation from
surface water, land
surfaces, and vegetation**

rain

**use by
humans**

**evaporation
from oceans**

lakes

well

water table

fresh groundwater

**salty
groundwater**

rivers flow to oceans

▲ *Water circulates between the oceans, land, and atmosphere. Without the water cycle providing freshwater, life on Earth would not be possible.*

mountain stream. These are often the sources of rivers, which continue to carry the water down toward the ocean under the force of gravity.

Rivers and streams are also fed by runoff, which is rainwater that trickles across the surface of land directly into the rivers. However, rain that reaches the ground sinks into the soil. Some of it will be absorbed by plants, which need water to stay alive. However, the water that goes into plants is soon released again into the air through holes in the leaves. This process is called transpiration.

▶ *These underground caverns are flooded with groundwater. Water dripping through rocks produces stalactites and stalagmites. These build up from minerals in the groundwater to form columns that hang down (stalactites) and pillars that rise up (stalagmites).*

Groundwater

Some rainwater seeps deeper through the soil into the rocks below. It then becomes groundwater. Some rocks, such as sandstone, are porous, which means they contain many tiny spaces, similar to a sponge. Water can seep into these spaces. Other rocks, such as limestone, are not porous but are permeable, which means water can flow through them. Water also flows through cracks in the rocks and into caves. Some rocks are impermeable, which means that water cannot flow through them. Impermeable rocks include clay and granite.

Water seeps through permeable rocks until the rocks become saturated—full of water. Rocks become saturated when impermeable rocks beneath stop the water from sinking farther down. The saturated rocks are called aquifers. Even in the aquifer, the water continues to flow downhill toward the ocean, like it would in a river on the surface.

Water table

The saturated zone is called the water table. In wet lowlands, the water table may be only a few feet below the soil, while in mountain regions, it may be hundreds of feet down. The water table also rises and falls according to the amount of rainfall.

The water table also follows the shape of the land, arching upward under hills. Wells are drilled down to the water table to obtain water in aquifers.

Some of the water trapped in aquifers has been there for thousands of years. Beneath many desert regions, there are underground water resources that accumulated during the last ice age, when the climate was much wetter than today. When this water is removed, the wells will run dry.

Where the water table meets the surface, swamps, lakes, and springs form. Springs are flows of groundwater up to the surface. They often occur at the base of hills.

When water percolates slowly through porous rocks, such as sandstone, the water is filtered and impurities are removed. This means that spring water is usually safe to drink. However, water that seeps through limestone is not filtered in this way.

Water from some wells and springs is warm. This water is hot because the ground gets 1°F warmer every 65 feet (1°C every 36 meters) below the ground. Many hot springs occur in volcanic regions. There, groundwater seeps down toward pockets of hot melted rocks called magma. The water that comes out of some volcanic springs is often near the boiling point.

Geysers are hot springs that erupt into the air as columns of water and steam. Yellowstone National Park in Wyoming has many geysers. They are formed when the groundwater is heated above the boiling point so that it is turned into steam.

Interruptions to the water cycle

All water that reaches the land from the oceans eventually returns to them. Some human activities interrupt the cycle and delay the return of some of the water for long periods. An example is the construction of dams across rivers. Artificial lakes, called reservoirs, form behind the dams. The water is used to supply cities, farms, and factories.

See also: CLOUD • GLACIATION • OCEAN • RAIN AND RAINFALL • WATER SUPPLY

Water supply

For thousands of years, water was taken directly from natural sources—rivers, lakes, streams, and wells. In many parts of the world, people still get their water from these sources. As societies grew and became more industrialized, however, much more water was needed, and it had to be clean. So water supply systems were built to store and provide clean water for use in cities and towns.

Demand for water has increased considerably over the years, partly because there are more people, but also because there is more interest in cleanliness and hygiene and because most industrial processes need huge amounts of water. When water is easily available, people use more of it. Those who must bring water into the home from an outside source limit usage to small amounts. When water is no farther away than a faucet, however, each person can use an average of 50 gallons (230 liters) a day.

Therefore, it is necessary to ensure that there is enough water for all these needs (though there are many parts of the world that are still unable to do so). Water must be stored so that a dry spell of weather does not mean a severe water shortage. Water is collected in reservoirs (artificial lakes) that maintain a regular supply to homes and factories.

The reservoirs are often made by building dams across mountain valleys. From the reservoir, the water is piped to a pumping station outside the town. Because the reservoirs may be up in the mountains, it is sometimes necessary to have pressure breaks, or other smaller reservoirs. These ensure that the water arriving through the faucet in a person's home is not at too high a pressure.

From the pumping station, the water goes to a service reservoir. Generally, this is higher than the town it supplies. Otherwise the water is pumped into a tall water tower. From its high position the water can flow down to houses, rather than needing to be pumped. Large pipes, called mains, lead to the streets of the town, and each house has its own separate service pipe that connects it to the main pipe under the street.

◀ *This water treatment plant near Cape Town, South Africa, stores water in round tanks, where any solid material settles to the bottom before the water is purified.*

DID YOU KNOW?

Distillation occurs when water is heated so that it changes from a liquid to a gas. The gas (water vapor) consists only of water and does not contain any of the materials that were dissolved in the water, such as salt or dirt. If the vapor is then collected and cooled so that it turns back into a liquid, the resulting water will be pure. This process is expensive because a lot of energy is needed to boil the water.

However, the temperature at which water boils falls as the pressure on the liquid falls. This is because the lower the pressure on the surface of the water, the less energy is needed for the vapor to escape. In recent years, this principle has been applied to produce more efficient distillation plants for the desalination of seawater.

In a typical system, preheated saltwater is forced into a low-pressure chamber, where some of the water immediately vaporizes. This vapor then condenses into pure water on cold pipes carrying the new seawater into the system. This is done several times, in chambers that have lower and lower pressure.

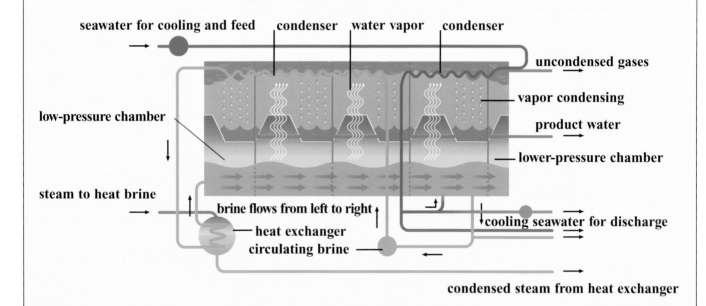

▲ *In this flash-chamber evaporator, the brine moves from one chamber to the next, each of which is at a lower pressure than the previous one.*

Cleaning the water

It is important to ensure that the water used for drinking, cooking, and washing is clean. As well as dirt, water can carry microorganisms that cause diseases such as dysentery, typhoid, and cholera, and these must be removed.

Before it reaches the reservoir, water is passed through a coarse screen to get rid of leaves and other debris. Just being kept in the reservoir helps clean the water because large solids sink to the bottom in a process called sedimentation. The water is then passed through grains of carbon, which remove bad smells. Often, it is then treated with chlorine, which kills many harmful bacteria.

The water is then passed through a microstrainer. This is a very fine stainless steel mesh. It removes many tiny organisms, such as worms and algae. Even smaller particles, such as clay, may remain.

They are removed by flocculation, which involves adding chemicals that make the particles clump together. These larger clumps settle to the bottom.

Filtration

The water, now very clear, is then passed through a series of filters. They may be slow or rapid. A rapid filter contains three layers—fine sand, followed by coarser sand, followed by a layer of coal. Any remaining harmful bacteria collect in a layer at the top of the filter.

Most filters are rapid, but slow filters are more effective. Although the process takes much longer, slow-filtered water needs no further purification.

Aeration and sterilization

Filtered water is then passed through an aerator, which bubbles oxygen through it. The water is then sterilized with more chlorine to kill any remaining bacteria. However, chlorinated water smells and tastes unpleasant, and the excess chlorine must be removed. Ozone gas is also used to sterilize water in some water-treatment plants. This does not produce unpleasant odors, but it is expensive.

In the United States, many water supplies are also treated with fluorine, which helps to strengthen people's teeth and prevent tooth decay.

Softening

Natural water is often "hard," which means it contains a lot of dissolved calcium and magnesium salts. These metals react with chemicals in soap and stop the soap from producing a lather. Hard water also tastes different, and the chemicals in it form residues in pipes and washing machines.

In many areas, water is softened. This can be done by adding lime, which reacts with the dissolved salts to make a solid scum that can be removed. Another way is to pass water through resins, which remove the calcium from the water.

▶ *Freshwater is stored in artificial lakes called reservoirs. These are formed by building dams across rivers. The dams, such as this one in Scotland, will hold back the water flow down the river to make a deep lake.*

◄ *Wadi Rum in Jordan is one of the driest places on Earth, but crops can be grown there using modern irrigation techniques. Circular patches of land are kept fertile with water piped to the region from elsewhere.*

Water and farming

In areas that do not get enough rain, the land cannot be farmed without irrigation. This is a process that uses water from rivers or wells to water crops. The first irrigation projects were developed by ancient civilizations that sprang up around the Nile River in Egypt, the Tigris and Euphrates rivers in Iraq, and the Indus River in Pakistan. The first irrigation works in the Western Hemisphere were built about two thousand years ago in Mexico, Bolivia, and Peru.

About one-quarter of the world's farmland is now irrigated. As well as making farming possible in dry areas, irrigation is also used to boost the growth of crops in areas that do not get a reliable supply of rain.

Irrigation methods

Most of the world's irrigation projects involve dams built on rivers to trap water and canal systems to lead the water to farmland. For example, the Hoover Dam on the Colorado River and the All American Canal made the arid Imperial Valley in California a rich farming region.

An increasing amount of irrigation water comes from below-ground sources. Groundwater is found in rocks, such as limestone, which contain many cracks and caves, and in porous rocks, such as sandstone, which contain spaces between the grains of sand. When these rocks are filled with water, they are known as aquifers.

Mechanical pumps are used to move water, but they are expensive to operate. Many farms use overhead sprinklers. They are light, are easily moved, and can disperse water over a wide area.

Pipes with several holes in them are also laid under the surface to carry water directly to plant roots. Underground irrigation prevents the water from evaporating away. However, it only works in flat areas, where water does not run away.

Another system used to reduce evaporation is overflooding. Fields are watered at night, when air temperatures are at their lowest. Another system is the drip and trickle system, in which a network of narrow plastic pipes on the ground leads water to individual plants or groups of plants. The spaces between the plants are left dry so that no water is wasted, and the amount of water supplied to the plants is precisely measured. This method is also useful in supplying fertilizers to the plant roots.

Covering plants with plastic helps to prevent water from being lost. Beneath plastic covers, the air becomes humid, and moisture condenses on the underside, dripping back onto the plants.

Problems caused by irrigation

In many areas, irrigation water slowly raises the amount of salt in the soil. When a soil is too salty, plants will not grow. Another problem with salt occurs near the coast. Draining groundwater lets seawater flood into the underground aquifers, gradually making the water more salty.

In many dry areas, the groundwater now being used is not being replaced by rainfall. Eventually, this water supply will run out. Building dams to collect water for irrigation also changes the way water flows and damages the river's wildlife.

See also: DAM • ION AND IONIZATION • POLLUTION • SEWAGE TREATMENT • WATER • WATER CYCLE

Wave motion

When most people hear the word *wave*, they usually think of an ocean wave or a wave of the hand. However, light and sound also travel in waves, as do shock waves from an earthquake. Scientists have even discovered that the tiny particles, such as electrons, that make up atoms can also act in a similar way to waves. All waves are regular disturbances that carry energy.

All waves repeat themselves in space and time. This can be seen by observing the regular succession of ocean waves. There are three ways to describe the characteristics of waves: the wave-length, the wave speed, and the frequency. All these factors are closely related. The wavelength is the distance through which the wave repeats itself, that is, the distance from the peak of one wave to the peak of the next. Some waves may have wavelengths that are many miles long, while others are just a tiny fraction of an inch long. The height of the wave peak is called the amplitude, and the time it takes a wave to move the distance of one wavelength is called the period.

The frequency is the number of times the wave completes one wavelength in a second. The frequency can be calculated by dividing one by the

▼ A surfer rides a huge ocean wave. The crest of the wave is moving through the water. As the wave reaches the coastline, the water will become too shallow for the wave, and the wave will break.

TYPES OF WAVES

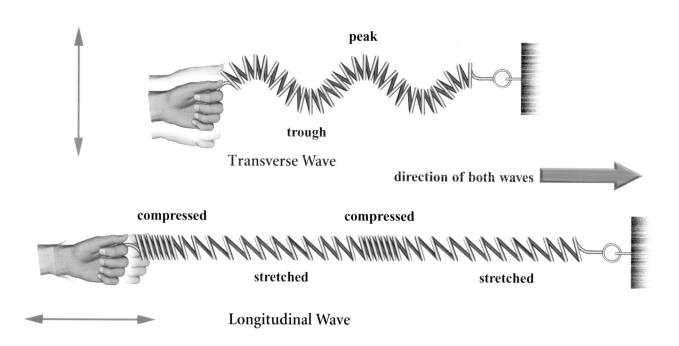

peak

trough

Transverse Wave

direction of both waves

compressed   compressed

stretched   stretched

Longitudinal Wave

▲ *There are two types of waves. Transverse waves oscillate in a medium at right angles to the direction of travel. Ocean waves are transverse waves. Longitudinal waves stretch and compress in a medium in the same plane as the direction of travel. Sound waves are longitudinal waves.*

period. If the period is half a second, for example, the frequency will be two. Frequency is measured in hertz (Hz). One hertz is one wavelength per second.

It is also important to know the speed at which the wave crests are moving forward. The speed in a particular direction is call the velocity. The wavelength, frequency, and velocity of any wave are all related by the equation:

$$\text{wavelength} = \text{frequency} \times \text{velocity}$$

Types of waves

Most waves are vibrations passing through a medium (substance) such as air, water, or rock. There are two ways in which the vibration can be carried forward through the medium.

For example, the wave crests of ocean waves traveling through deep water move forward with a particular velocity. However, the individual water molecules making up the sea do not actually move forward at all. They simply vibrate up and down, sending the motion of the wave along to the next

molecule. When a boat floats on a wave, it bobs up and down but does not actually move along with the wave. This type of wave is a transverse wave.

The waves on a beach are slightly different. There the wave breaks because the water is not deep enough for the wave to continue. Instead, the wave trough begins to drag along the bottom and slow down. The wave crest continues at the same speed and tumbles into the trough in front. The water breaking on a beach does continue to move backward and forward. However, this motion is not really a wave because the vibration is not being transmitted farther along.

Sound waves are carried in a different way. They compress and expand the medium so the molecules vibrate in the same direction as the wave is traveling. This type of wave is a longitudinal wave. The ears detect the waves traveling through the air, and the brain turns them into the sounds people hear.

Visible light is a beam of tiny particles called photons. Photons are packets of energy that are released from atoms. The photons can move

◄ Astronomers study the universe by detecting the waves that arrive from space. Light beams are waves, as are other forms of radiation produced by stars, such as X-rays and ultraviolet light.

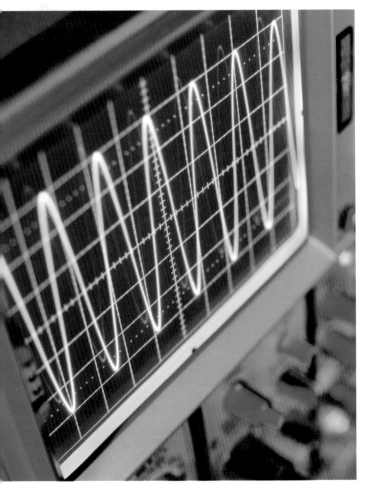

through a vacuum (empty space) and do not need a medium in which to travel. Although the photons travel in straight lines, the electric and magnetic fields that the particles produce move as transverse waves. This gives beams of light the same properties as other waves.

Interference

All waves show the phenomenon of interference. This happens when two or more waves meet. The two waves combine to form a single wave.

This can either be constructive interference, which makes the new wave bigger than the original waves, or destructive interference, in which the two waves cancel each other out. The type of interference produced depends on the phase of the two waves. If

◄ This oscilloscope is a machine for converting the movement of invisible waves, such as radio waves, to moving lines on a screen. It does this by converting the wave motion into an electrical current. The electrical current is used to control a magnet inside the oscilloscope. The magnet directs a beam of electrons onto the screen showing the wavelength, frequency, speed, and shape of the original wave.

WAVE INTERFERENCE

Constructive Interference

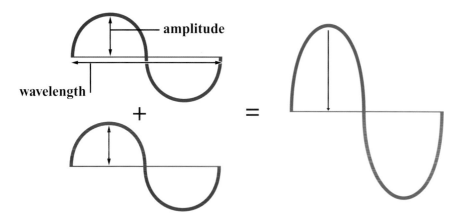

amplitude

wavelength

+

=

Destructive Interference

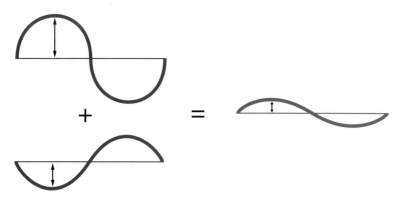

+

=

◄ *Interference occurs when two waves meet. Depending on their phases, waves either combine or cancel each other out. The result is a single wave in which the amplitude is the sum of the amplitudes of the two original waves. If waves are in phase, they interfere constructively; if the waves are out of phase, they interfere destructively.*

the crests of two waves of the same wavelength and frequency touch when the waves meet each other, the waves are in phase. If the crest of one wave meets the trough of the other, then the waves are out of phase. Waves that are in phase interfere constructively. The two wave crests combine to make a single crest with double the amplitude of the original waves. Destructive interference occurs when waves are out of phase. The crest combines with the trough to make no wave at all.

Waves with different wavelengths and frequencies cannot be completely in phase with each other. Instead, they interfere to form a complex motion made up of several superimposed waves.

Diffraction

This property of waves involves waves moving through a gap that is less than the wavelength of the waves passing through. As it does so, the wave spreads out in a sphere as it would from its original source. A grill consisting of very thin slits, called a diffraction grating, is used to diffract light. The diffracted light then interferes with itself to form a pattern of bright and dark areas.

In 1801, English scientist Thomas Young (1773–1829) used diffraction to show that light moved as waves. He shined light from a lamp onto two thin slits (similar to those in a diffraction grating) and saw a pattern of light and dark bands on a screen. The bright areas were where the two waves were in phase—producing bright light by constructive interference—and the dark areas were where they were out of phase—resulting in destructive interference that canceled out any light waves.

See also: MUSICAL INSTRUMENT • REFLECTION AND REFRACTION • SOUND • SPRING • WAVE POWER

Wave power

As the world's supplies of fossil fuels start to run out, scientists are looking for sources of renewable energy such as the Sun, wind, and waves. Since the 1970s, devices to capture the mighty power of the ocean waves have been designed and tested, but the technology is not yet practical for large-scale use.

The energy of ocean waves comes from the Sun. The Sun heats the surface of Earth unevenly, causing winds that whip the sea up into waves. Gradually, the waves build up over long stretches of ocean, and the energy they contain depends on how long and how high they are. The size of waves, and thus their energy, varies greatly around the world.

Two of the best places for capturing wave power are coastal Scotland and the waters surrounding Japan. In both areas, the waves can reach heights of 80 feet (25 meters) or more—higher than an eight-story building. Wave-energy collectors placed off the coast of the Scottish Hebrides over a distance of 50 miles (80 kilometers) could supply more than 1,000 megawatts (1 billion watts) of power. This is easily as much as a large power plant would produce by burning fossil fuels.

So far, most research into wave power has been concentrated on the supply of electrical power to the national grids in the countries in which the research is taking place. Energy from the waves could also be used as a local source of power, such

▼ *Waves possess two types of energy—kinetic and potential energy—that can be used to generate electricity. Designing devices to capture this energy is difficult because waves can be very unpredictable.*

◄ The Osprey, seen here being towed to its installation site, is an oscillating water column device. Waves rush into its central chamber and push air through a turbine. The Osprey can generate two megawatts of electricity.

as for a floating chemical or water-purification plant that might be too far from the mainland to be connected to the national grid.

The only commercially operating wave power plant is situated on the Scottish island of Islay. A number of sites are being tested in Japan, Norway, and the Portuguese Azores.

Wave power plants

A wave power plant consists of a number of wave energy converters, which are either afloat but moored to the seabed or mounted on the seabed. The converters change the back-and-forth motion of the waves into a smooth, continuous one-way motion suitable for producing electricity. The electrical output from the converters is sent ashore to a substation feeding the national grid.

A good converter should be small compared to the amount of power it can produce and tough enough to survive in rough seas for long periods

OSCILLATING WATER COLUMN

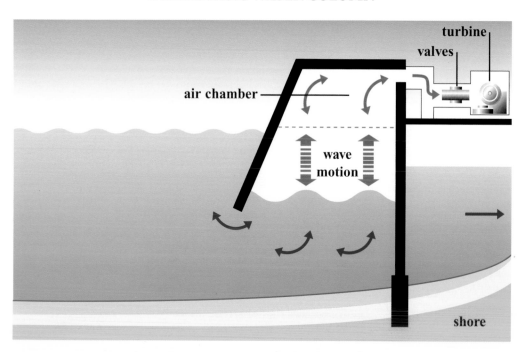

turbine

valves

air chamber

wave motion

shore

◄ In an oscillating water column, the rise and fall of water inside the shore-based structure pushes and pulls air through a system of valves to drive a turbine.

without needing a great deal of maintenance. Many different designs for converters have been developed, but the major ones are the oscillating water column, the tapered channel, the duck, the raft, and the flexible air bag.

Oscillating water column

At its simplest, an oscillating water column (OWC) is a long, upright tube with the top open to the air and the bottom below the surface open to the sea. As a wave passes, water inside the tube rises and falls, drawing in or blowing out air under pressure at the top. Mounted on top of the tube is an air turbine, which is connected to a generator. The turbine is turned by the air current.

Some OWCs are floating, while others are fixed to the seafloor. The underwater types are better protected against stormy weather, but there is less and less wave energy to collect as the water gets deeper. OWCs are simple and have few moving parts. The Limpet plant on Islay, Scotland, is based on the OWC principle. It can generate around 500 kilowatts of energy, which is enough to power three hundred houses.

The tapered channel

The tapered channel, or TAPCHAN, works in a similar way to a hydroelectric power (HEP) plant. The device has a broad entry channel that narrows as waves move into it. The water spills over the channel and into a reservoir. The reservoir is above sea level, and electricity is generated by dropping the water through a turbine and back into the sea.

One drawback of the tapered channel is that it is not suitable for all coastlines. This type of device needs consistent waves that have a good wave energy. It also needs enough space around it to site a reservoir close to the shore.

▼ *Salter's duck is a type of float that bobs up and down in the water. The energy of the waves is converted into electricity by a dynamo, with power being generated on the up and down strokes.*

COCKERELL'S RAFT

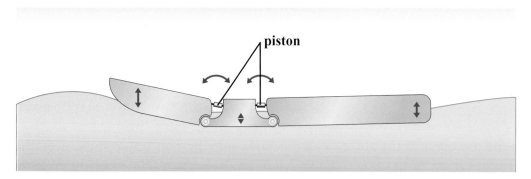

piston

◄ *The pontoons of each Cockerell's raft are connected by pistons. Wave motion acts on these pistons, making them pump fluid into a hydraulic generator.*

The duck

Salter's duck, named after its inventor, South African–born Scottish physicist Stephen Salter (1938–), was developed at Edinburgh University, Scotland. A single duck is a float, which is pear-shaped when seen from the side.

All the ducks are mounted on a floating tube, with their beaks (sharp ends) facing the oncoming waves. The motion of the waves causes the ducks to nod up and down, and it is the energy of this nodding motion that is converted into electricity. The smooth, curved rear of the ducks ensures that no waves are reflected. Most of the wave energy—around 80 percent—is absorbed. Each duck can nod independently of the others, and if built full-size would be as large as a family house.

Inside the beak, four gyroscopes flip back and forth with their own spinning movement as the duck rocks up and down. The rapid back-and-forth motion works an oil pump to produce hydraulic power for a generator. The power can also be used to increase the speed of the gyros when the output of electricity is at its greatest. In effect, this stores surplus energy, which can then be withdrawn later as needed to drive the generator. Thus the output of electricity can be controlled, even though the wave energy that produces it cannot.

The raft

Simpler than the duck and also still in the experimental stage are the raft designs, such as Cockerell's raft. These systems usually consist of a large, flat rectangular pontoon, with two smaller pontoons hinged to it. The pontoons are moored in line with the direction of the wind. As waves pass under the raft, the smaller sections move up and down, and again the force of this motion is used to work a hydraulic pump that drives a turbine connected to an electricity generator.

The raft is capable of generating over a million watts of electricity, but to do so, it must be as large as 500 feet (150 meters) long by 165 feet (50 meters) wide. Otherwise, the main pontoon will not be stable enough to hold its position when the smaller sections are forced up and down by the movement of the waves. However, this makes the raft an expensive way of capturing wave power.

Flexible air bag

Made of flexible rubber, the air bag lies head-on to the sea so that waves pass along its length. The inside of the air bag is divided into compartments, which are pushed together by the rising water and then released as the wave falls. In this way, the air pressure in the compartments changes all the time, and the pressure differences can be used to drive an air turbine and generate electricity.

The air bag is fairly small—650 feet (200 meters) long—so it has the advantage of being one of the cheapest designs. However, there are problems with finding a flexible rubber material strong enough to stand up to the waves for long periods of time. The design must also ensure that the air bag stays at the correct angle to the waves.

See also: GYROSCOPE • POWER GENERATION AND DISTRIBUTION • TIDAL POWER • WAVE MOTION

Weathering

In one person's lifetime, the landscape may seem to be unchanging. All the time, however, hills and mountains are being worn down and shaped by various kinds of weathering and erosion. Elsewhere, rock debris is swept into lakes and seas, where it settles and compresses to form new rocks.

Geomorphologists (people who study landforms and how landscapes are molded) often use the terms *weathering* and *erosion* together. The two types of processes are closely connected and, as such, are commonly misunderstood. However, weathering and erosion are distinctly different.

Weathering is the decay or disintegration (break down) of Earth's surface, primarily rocks and soil, in its original position. The decay of Earth's surface is known as chemical weathering, while the disintegration of surface material is called physical or mechanical weathering.

Erosion is the denudation (wearing away) of Earth's surface. This involves a wider set of processes than weathering. Erosion includes the decay and disintegration of surface material by natural forces including weathering but also running water, sea waves, and moving ice. Importantly, erosion also includes the removal of the resulting material elsewhere as it falls, blows, is washed away, or is moved by glaciers from its original position.

While eroded material is being removed and transported, it may also contribute to further erosion by wearing away other surface material by

▼ *This mountain ridge in the Mount Baker Wilderness Area, Washington, shows many signs of significant weathering. The mountain rock has been decayed and disintegrated by both chemical and mechanical weathering processes, producing broad scree slopes.*

abrasion (grinding). Particles of eroded material are also broken down into smaller pieces as they collide with each other. This erosional process is called attrition.

Effects of weathering and erosion

Geologists have calculated that Earth is around 4.6 billion years old. Over vast time spans, mountains have been raised up from sediments on ancient seabeds, only to be worn down to nearly flat plains by erosion. The wearing away of the land is continuing all the time.

Weathering is the fundamental (basic) process involved in the wearing down and molding of Earth's surface. Weathering produces huge amounts of loose rock and soil, which the agents of erosion can then remove, use to further wear away the land, and deposit elsewhere.

CHEMICAL WEATHERING

Chemical weathering is the decay of rocks and soil by chemical processes. Chemical weathering is primarily caused by the chemical reactions between rocks and water.

Although some minerals, such as halite (rock salt), are soluble (can be dissolved) in pure water, most minerals and rocks have to undergo some chemical change before this can happen. Rainwater is the main agent of chemical weathering, but rainwater is not pure water. Rainwater contains both oxygen (O_2) and carbon dioxide (CO_2), as well as other chemicals, dissolved from the air. If rainwater seeps through soil to underlying rock, it dissolves more carbon dioxide and other substances. The concentration of carbon dioxide in the soil is usually between ten and one-hundred times greater than the concentration of carbon dioxide in the air. These chemical characteristics are what make rainwater such an effective weathering agent.

Only a few minerals resist decay caused by chemical weathering. One of them is quartz. This hard mineral is one of the chief minerals in granite. When granite decays, bits of quartz that are left behind are carried down to the sea by rivers. There they build up along the shore to become the main component of sandy beaches.

Oxidation

One type of chemical weathering is known as oxidation. Oxidation commonly occurs with oxygen, which reacts easily with many other substances. Iron is the most widely oxidized mineral element. The oxidation of iron is called rusting and produces a characteristic yellowish-brown to red color on the surface of the iron. Other readily oxidized mineral elements include aluminum, chromium, magnesium, and sulfur.

◀ *This unusual rock formation in Alberta, Canada, has been formed by chemical weathering by rainwater. In a process called hydrolysis, acid in the rainwater reacts with minerals in the rock, allowing the minerals to be dissolved by the rainwater. Over time, this process has caused the rock to be eroded into a pattern of vertical grooves and pleats.*

Rusting occurs when iron is exposed to moist air or rain. Dissolved oxygen in the water reacts with iron to form iron (III) oxide (Fe_2O_3). The reaction is as follows:

$$2FeO + O_2 \rightarrow Fe_2O_3$$
iron (II) oxide (ferrous iron) + oxygen $\rightarrow$ iron (III) oxide (ferric iron)

Rusting weakens iron minerals in rocks, causing them to crumble and allowing them to be washed away in solution with water. This exposes further, underlying iron to rusting. Over time, rusting leads to the disintegration of iron-rich rocks.

Hydration

Another form of chemical weathering is called hydration. Hydration is the process whereby minerals in rock absorb water. This makes them expand (swell) and/or sometimes chemically change. One example of hydration is the alteration of anhydrite (a mineral comprised primarily of copper sulfate; $CuSO_4$) to gypsum. The reaction is as follows:

▲ *The Reed Flute Cave in an area of limestone in Guanxi Province, China, is a good example of chemical weathering. During a process called carbonation, limestone is dissolved by rainwater, often producing spectacular caves with stalagtites and stalagmites.*

$$CaSO_4 + 2H_2O \rightarrow CaSO_4.2H_2O$$
anhydrite + water $\rightarrow$ gypsum

Where there is no chemical reaction involved with hydration, the process may still cause mechanical weathering. This is because many rocks and soils expand when they absorb water. Some materials, especially those containing clays, may expand up to sixteen times their original size. Expansion weakens the materials and may cause them to fracture and even become fluid.

Hydrolysis

Hydrolysis is a form of chemical weathering that occurs when acidic water decays rock minerals. Minerals vulnerable to hydrolysis include amphiboles, feldspars, and pyroxenes. Orthoclase feldspars, for example, are common in igneous rocks such as granite. During hydrolysis, the orthoclase feldspars in granite decay into kaolin, silica, and potash. The kaolin and silica remain, while the potash is removed in solution with water. Quartz and mica—the other two significant minerals found in granite—are unaffected by hydrolysis, but the decay of the feldspar, which is integral to the structure of granite, eventually causes the remaining rock to crumble apart. The reaction is as follows:

$$2KAlSi_3O_8 + 2H_2O \rightarrow$$
$$Al_2Si_2O_5(OH)_4 + 4SiO_2 + K_2O$$
orthoclase feldspar + water $\rightarrow$
kaolin + silica + potash

Carbonation

Another major type of chemical weathering is carbonation. Carbonation is similar to hydrolysis but occurs to rocks that contain calcium carbonate ($CaCO_3$), such as limestone and chalk. Carbonation is responsible for creating limestone caves. Carbonation occurs when rain combines with carbon dioxide or an organic acid to form a weak carbonic acid, which goes on to react with limestone, forming calcium bicarbonate, which is soluble in water. The reaction is as follows:

$$CO_2 + H_2O \rightarrow H_2CO_3$$
carbon dioxide + water $\rightarrow$ carbonic acid

$$H_2CO_3 + CaCO_3 \rightarrow Ca(HCO_3)_2$$
carbonic acid + calcium carbonate $\rightarrow$
calcium bicarbonate

Bare limestone surfaces are often split apart by grooves worn out in this way. Sometimes small patches of soil appear. These soils include impurities left behind after carbonation. Called weathering residues, they consist of such substances as quartz, clay, and occasionally insoluble iron hydroxides—"red earths."

The effects of chemical weathering

Rainwater that seeps through the cracks in limestone enlarges vertical joints and horizontal bedding planes into networks of chimneys, tunnels, and caverns. Some of these caverns have features made up of calcium carbonate, which is deposited from the seeping water. The most familiar of these features are the icicle-like stalactites, which hang from the ceilings of limestone caves, and the stalagmites, which grow upward from the floors of the caves.

◄ *This rock face has been roughened because of the effects of physical weathering. The rock is likely weathered due to a combination of thermal expansion and contraction, caused by changes in temperature, and by frost shattering, as water freezes in cracks in the rock and expands.*

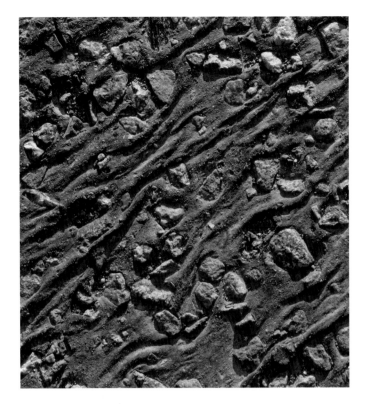

◄ Heavy rainfall can be a cause of weathering. As raindrops hit soft ground, they may loosen soil and rock particles and form channels called rills.

It is not necessary to visit a limestone cave to see the effects of chemical weathering. They can be seen on old stone buildings, monuments, and tombstones—especially those with lettering on them. Weathering weakens rocks, particularly when some minerals break down, while other rocks remain unaffected. Such rocks then become open to mechanical weathering and the agents of erosion.

MECHANICAL WEATHERING

Mechanical weathering occurs because of destructive forces being applied to rocks and soils by various factors, including wind, rainfall, temperature changes, and biological factors.

Exfoliation

In dry regions, rocks are heated by the Sun during the day. The various minerals in coarse-grained rocks, such as granite, expand by varying amounts. As a result, the surface cracks and eventually layers of rock peel away. This process is called exfoliation. Exfoliation also takes place at night, when the rocks cool rapidly. Because the minerals in the rocks contract (shrink) at differing rates, the rocks start to break apart, making loud cracking sounds like pistol shots. Exfoliation by thermal expansion and contraction can occur anywhere, even when water is present, but it is most noticeable in hot deserts.

Frost shattering

In cold, moist regions, frost shattering is the chief form of mechanical weathering. Water collects in crevices in surface rocks during the day. At night, the temperature may drop below freezing point and the water freezes. Because ice occupies 9 percent more space than the same quantity of water, freezing makes the water expand. This expansion puts tremendous pressure on both sides of the cracks. The cracks are gradually widened by a number of freeze-thaw cycles, until eventually the rocks split apart.

Large-scale frost shattering is especially effective in mountain regions where jointed (cracked) rocks are exposed on the surface. Chunks of shattered rock that have broken away from steep slopes tumble downhill and pile up at the bottoms of the slopes. These great heaps of rubble are called talus or scree. This loose material is later removed by landslides, running water, or glaciers.

Wind and rain

Wind and rain can play a role in weathering. Although wind is mostly an agent of erosion, transporting fine debris and aiding abrasion and attrition, wind can also cause weathering by plucking particles of soil or sand from where they are set and by deforming soft land surfaces.

DID YOU KNOW?

The average rate of erosion of Earth's surface is about 1 foot (0.3 meter) every four hundred years. In warm and wet areas, however, this rate speeds up dramatically. In cold areas, it takes many thousands of years for the same amount of land to erode.

▶ *As this tree is growing, its roots are penetrating downward through cracks in the underlying rock. As the roots widen, they force the cracks apart, causing the rock to slowly disintegrate. This process is a type of biological weathering.*

Likewise, precipitation is also responsible for some mechanical weathering. As raindrops, sleet, or hail fall onto soft ground, they can move soil or rock particles apart. As rainwater runs off drainage slopes, it may further disturb the surface, forming small drainage channels called rills. Large amounts of rainfall can also weaken soils and some rocks by the process of hydration.

Biological weathering

Plant roots also cause mechanical weathering. For example, a young tree may take root in a crack in a boulder. As the tree grows, the roots push downward and sideways. This force widens the crack in the boulder.

Worms and other burrowing animals also play a part in mechanical weathering because they loosen fine particles of rock and bring them to the surface. There the rock is often quickly removed by the agents of erosion. This occurs especially on bare surfaces. In regions covered by plants, however, roots tend to bind soil particles together. By protecting the surface, plants reduce the rate of erosion.

Rates of weathering

The rates of weathering vary from place to place. This is because the factors that determine the rates of weathering and erosion also vary locally. These factors include atmosphere, climate, geology (rock types), pedology (soil characteristics), topography (land features), hydrology (the properties and distribution of water on Earth's surface, underground, and in the atmosphere), and vegetation.

The amount of moisture in the atmosphere has a influence on weathering, as does the concentrations of various gases that can combine with the moisture. The mineral composition and texture of a rock will determine the rate of its alteration or disintegration, as will the pattern of joints, fractures, and fissures within it. Climate will also control the type and rate of weathering by affecting the chance of exfoliation, freeze-thaw cycles, and chemical reactions.

See also: EROSION • GEOLOGY • GLACIATION • MOUNTAIN • RAIN AND RAINFALL • RIVER AND LAKE • SOIL • WIND

Weather system

Weather is the condition of the air hour by hour, day by day. Stormy, wet weather one day may be followed by calm, dry weather the next day. Weather conditions are associated with particular weather systems. Understanding weather systems helps meteorologists predict the weather.

Most of the weather on Earth is the result of changing conditions in the troposphere. The troposphere is the lowest layer in the atmosphere (the blanket of gases that surrounds Earth). The study of the atmosphere, weather, and weather systems is called meteorology.

The main elements involved in weather are air pressure, temperature, wind speed and direction, and the amount of moisture in the air (humidity). The temperature of air is determined by the Sun. The Sun's heat is most intense around the equator and least intense at the poles. Warm air is lighter (less dense) than cold air. In tropical regions, the Sun heats Earth's surface which, in turn, warms the air near the ground. This warm air rises, while other, cooler air flows in from the north and south to replace it.

In other parts of the world, air is moving downward. Air pressure (the weight of the air pushing down in one place) is high where air is

▼ *These imposing, dark mammatus clouds over Tulsa, Oklahoma, are sometimes seen after thunderstorms have passed overhead.*

▲ *A blizzard in Canada is caused by cold weather systems moving south from the Arctic. The cold air freezes water droplets in the air before they reach the ground and, therefore, they fall as snow.*

sinking down, and it is low where warm air is rising. Air pressure is measured using instruments called barometers.

Winds are movements of air. Winds carry excess heat away from tropical regions toward the poles. They act like natural thermostats, ensuring that the tropics do not become overheated.

Winds also carry clouds. Clouds consist of suspended water droplets. Many clouds are formed over the sea, and winds carry these clouds to the land. Clouds bring supplies of freshwater to land areas in the form of precipitation (rain, sleet, snow, and hail). Without this supply of freshwater, there would be no life on land.

Air masses

Air masses are large bodies of air that have roughly the same characteristics at any one level, although conditions gradually change with altitude (height above Earth's surface). There are two chief types of air masses. Those forming over the continents are called continental air masses, and those forming over seas are called maritime air masses. These two types of air masses have different temperatures, pressures, and moisture levels. This is partly because land areas heat up and cool down faster than water surfaces, and also because air masses over water are more humid (moist) than those over land. Tropical continental air masses, therefore, are generally drier and warmer than tropical maritime air masses.

Fronts

The boundaries between air masses of contrasting types are called fronts. In both the Northern and Southern hemispheres, the boundary between the moist, warm air from the subtropics and the cold, heavy air from the poles is called the polar front. There, warm air rides up over the cold air. As the air rises, it cools; rain clouds form because cold air cannot hold as much water vapor as warm air. The cold air at the front surges under the warm

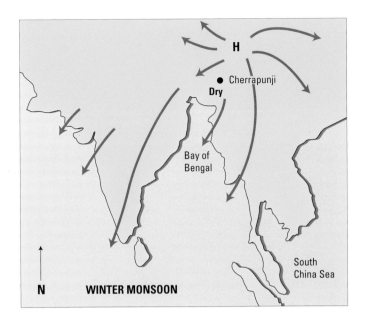

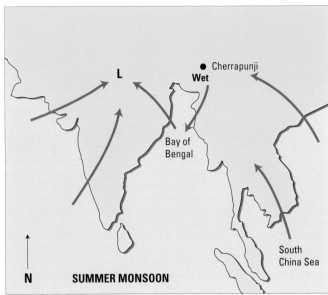

▲ *The maps above illustrate the changing annual wind-flow patterns associated with the winter and summer monsoons in southern Asia. Winds flow from high-pressure areas (H) to low-pressure areas (L).*

air and moves toward the tropics. There, it warms up, absorbs moisture, and eventually becomes tropical air. Therefore, the polar front is a place where warm and cold air masses are in conflict. It has changeable and often stormy weather.

Above the polar front, around the top of the troposphere, are strong winds called jet streams. These winds are often more than 100 miles (160 kilometers) wide and blow at up to 300 miles (485 kilometers) per hour. The jet stream flows in a westerly direction over the United States at a latitude 40 degrees North. However, its path varies greatly, and it often loops north and south.

Jet streams are important to airplane pilots. Pilots do not want to fly against jet streams because they slow planes down and make them use more fuel.

▶ *These illustrations show two types of depressions. Depressions consist of wedges of warm air with cold air behind and ahead of them. The edge of the advancing cold air is called a cold front, while the edge of the advancing warm air is called a warm front. Eventually, the cold front overtakes the warm front, and the warm air is lifted. This is called a cold occlusion. However, when the advancing cold air is not as cold as the cold air ahead of the warm front, the cold front rises above the warm front. This is called a warm occlusion.*

Air masses can move from the land to the sea or from the sea to the land. When such movements occur, there are changes in the air conditions including the lapse rate—the rate by which temperatures fall with increasing altitude. In warm regions, the lapse rate is sharp, while in cold regions it is gentle. When warm air moves over a cold surface, however, the lower layers of air may be so chilled that the temperatures may actually rise with height. This is called a temperature inversion. Water vapor in the air near the surface often condenses to form low clouds, mist, or fog. If an air mass moves over warm land, the lower layers are

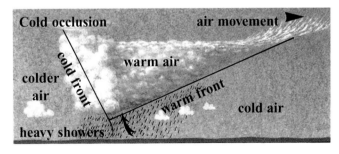

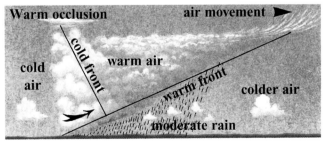

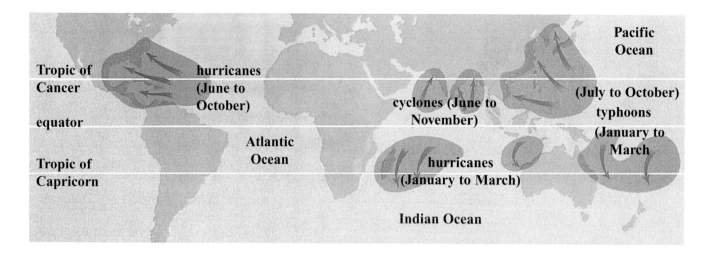

Tropic of Cancer

hurricanes (June to October)

equator

Atlantic Ocean

Tropic of Capricorn

cyclones (June to November)

hurricanes (January to March)

Indian Ocean

Pacific Ocean

(July to October) typhoons (January to March)

▲ *This map shows the areas of the world affected by tropical cyclones. These storms are also called hurricanes and typhoons, depending on where they occur.*

heated. This makes the lapse rate more extreme. Warm air then rises in strong updrafts, and towering storm clouds may develop as the water vapor rapidly condenses.

Depressions

Depressions are also called lows or cyclones. They are special kinds of weather systems with low air pressure. They may be up to 2,500 miles (4,000 kilometers) across. They enter the United States from the Pacific coast and bring with them weather that is often changeable.

Depressions form along the polar front, so they are features of the midlatitudes. In the Northern Hemisphere, they begin to develop when warm air blowing from the southwest flows into waves in the front. In this way, a wedge of warm air becomes enclosed in front and behind by cold air. In recent years, meteorologists have discovered that the waves occupied by the warm air conform with ripples in the jet stream going toward the poles, around 10 miles (16 kilometers) above the ground.

Meteorologists study the paths of jet streams, which help them predict the development and movements of depressions and their speed.

Soon, the warm and cold air bodies become interlocked to form a depression—a circular air mass in which air tends to be drawn toward the center

where the air pressure is lowest. However, because Earth is spinning on its axis, winds are deflected (turned away). This is called the Coriolis effect. As a result, the winds tend to circulate around the depression instead of blowing directly into it. In the Northern Hemisphere, the movement of air in depressions is counterclockwise. In the Southern Hemisphere, it is clockwise. Wind speeds depend on the intensity (strength) of the depression.

Air pressure

On weather maps, depressions appear as a series of concentric isobars (lines linking places with equal air pressure), with the lowest air pressure at the center of the depression. The pressure gradient (intensity of the depression) depends on the distance between the isobars. If they are closely packed together, the pressure gradient is high, and winds are strong. Where they are widely spaced, the pressure gradient is low, and winds are gentle.

The front edge of the warm air in the depression is called a warm front. The edge of the advancing cold air behind it is called a cold front. Because warm and cold air do not mix easily, the warm air rides upward over the cold air along the warm front. Behind it, the cold air pushes underneath the warm air along the cold front. Hence, warm air is rising along both fronts. This further reduces the air pressure and often intensifies the depression.

The warm, rising air cools, and water vapor condenses to form clouds. Both fronts are therefore bands of cloudy, rainy weather. Gradually, the cold front overtakes the warm front, usually pushing the warm air above ground level. This is called an occluded front or an occlusion. There, clouds and rain last for some time until the warm air cools and the clouds disappear. The depression then dies out.

Weather in depressions

No two depressions are exactly alike, but most bring a similar sequence of weather. The first sign of an advancing depression is often the appearance of high cirrus clouds. These wispy clouds, which consist of ice crystals, are often drawn out into long bands by the jet stream. As the warm front approaches, the clouds become progressively lower. The sequence of clouds is often cirrus first and then cirrostratus, altostratus, nimbostratus, and finally stratus.

As the warm front draws closer, rain starts to fall and steadily becomes heavier. After the warm front has passed, temperatures rise, and the air pressure stops falling. However, the arrival of the cold front brings more rainy weather and lower temperatures. The band of clouds along the cold front is narrower than the band of clouds along the warm front, but the weather is stormy. Cumulonimbus clouds are associated with thunder and lightning and bring heavy rain and stormy winds. After the cold front has passed, the air pressure rises, the humidity drops, and the skies clear.

Anticyclones

While depressions are associated with changeable weather, anticyclones are characterized by calm, settled weather. Anticyclones are high-air-pressure weather systems, and they are often called highs. Like depressions, highs appear on weather maps as a series of concentric isobars. In anticyclones, however, the highest air pressure is at the center.

Air tends to move outward from the center of an anticyclone. Again, the winds are deflected due to the Coriolis effect, and they tend to rotate around the center, that is, they blow in a direction roughly parallel to the isobars (not at right angles to them). The air circulates around anticyclones in a clockwise direction in the Northern Hemisphere and in a counterclockwise direction in the Southern Hemisphere. This is opposite to the air circulation in depressions.

▶ *This picture shows some of the widespread destruction caused by Hurricane Ivan in Florida on September 18, 2004. Many houses and larger buildings, such as the apartment complex in this picture, were devastated by the storm. Tropical cyclones, or hurricanes, are the most destructive type of weather system. They can be many miles in diameter and destroy entire communities.*

▲ *Tornados, or twisters, are powerful storm systems formed when cool, horizontally circulating winds pass over a warm, rising updraft and are lifted into a huge swirling vortex.*

In temperate regions, summer anticyclones are associated with fine weather, blue skies, light winds, and sunshine. In winter, however, the clear skies allow much of the heat received from the Sun during the day to escape into space at night. As a result, anticyclones often bring cold weather in winter. Frost, mist, and fog are also common. Because anticyclones are stable air masses, they often remain stationary (unmoving) for days on end. Advancing depressions are diverted to the north and south of them.

Large anticyclones build up in the high latitudes of the Northern Hemisphere in winter. These anticyclones in Canada and Siberia consist of cold and dense air. Other large anticyclones, which occur at latitudes 20 and 30 degrees North and South, contain warm air. There, air from the upper atmosphere is sinking and getting warmer. Land areas in these latitudes are often deserts. Air flows outward from these anticyclones, which prevents moist winds from coming in from the sea. These subtropical anticyclones move north and south according to the seasons.

Destructive weather systems

Other weather systems include tropical cyclones, also called hurricanes or typhoons. Cyclones are strong, low-pressure systems that do not have fronts. Cyclones develop over oceans between latitudes 5 and 25 degrees North and South. Scientists do not understand exactly why cyclones form, but these powerful storms with their fierce winds do much damage when they strike land areas. Destructive cyclones frequently occur in the Caribbean and in the eastern United States.

Tornados, sometimes called twisters, can be even more powerful than tropical cyclones. Compared to cyclones, they are small storms, seldom more than 2,600 feet (790 meters) across. However, the air pressure inside tornadoes is very low, and the fast-rising, spinning air reaches great speeds—fast enough to lift houses and people into the air. Tornados are common in the Midwest, where warm, moist air from the Gulf of Mexico flows northward across the surface at the same time as cold, dry air from the north flows over it.

See also: AIR • CLOUD • CYCLONE • METEOROLOGY • RAIN AND RAINFALL • TORNADO • WIND

Wegener, Alfred

Alfred Wegener is famous for his work describing the process of continental drift. He theorized that more than 200 million years ago, there was a single continent that later split into several pieces and began to move. He was among the first to consider continental drift in detail. This was a controversial idea that did not gain widespread acceptance until the 1950s. Wegener's influential theories inspired many scientists to gather new and important observations on the evolution of Earth.

▲ German geophysicist Alfred Wegener proposed the theory of continental drift in 1915.

Alfred Wegener was born in Berlin, Germany, in 1880. He studied at universities in Heidelberg and Innsbruck before gaining a doctorate in astronomy from the University of Berlin in 1904. However, his key interests proved to be meteorology (the study of the climate and weather) and geology (the study of Earth's physical structure).

After graduating, Wegener went to work in the Royal Prussian Aeronautical Observatory near Berlin, using kites and balloons to study the upper atmosphere. He also flew hot-air balloons, breaking a world record in 1906 with his brother Kurt by remaining aloft for more than 52 hours.

Later that year, Wegener joined a two-year expedition to Greenland's unmapped northeastern coast, the first of four such dangerous trips. He risked death on his second expedition in 1912 while climbing a glacier. As the first person to trace storm tracks over the ice cap, he amassed scientific data that established him as an international expert on polar meteorology and glaciology.

His expedition research also won Wegener a position at the University of Marberg in 1909, where he gave lively lectures on meteorology and astronomy. He was praised for his ability to convey complex ideas with great clarity. By the age of 30, Wegener collected his lectures into the acclaimed *Thermodynamics of the Atmosphere* (1912), which became a standard text in Germany.

While serving as a junior military officer in World War I (1914–1918), Wegener was wounded twice. On extended sick leave, he developed his theory of continental drift in his most important publication, *The Origin of Continents and Oceans* (1915). In this publication, Wegener rejected the accepted notion that the continents were once connected by large land bridges that had since sunk into the sea as Earth cooled and contracted. Wegener noted that continents move up and down to maintain equilibrium in a process called isostasy. He argued that these land bridges would have eventually reemerged.

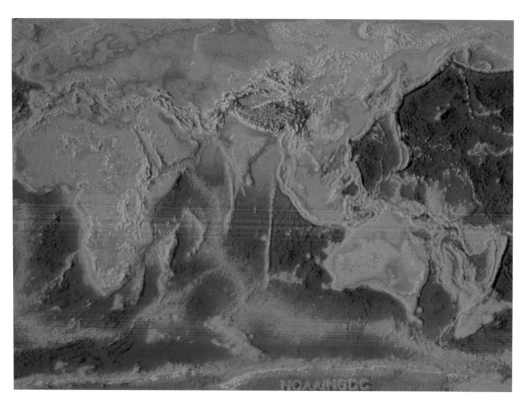

◀ *A computer-generated map shows some of the oceanic ridges that are forcing the continents apart. These are visible as lighter blue formations on the ocean floor and represent the boundaries between the plates carrying the continents and the oceanic floors. The Southeast Indian Ocean ridge runs almost horizontally between Australia and Antarctica (red area at bottom). Near Madagascar (the island to the right of Africa), it splits into the Southwest Indian Ocean ridge and the Carlsberg ridge.*

Instead, Wegener proposed that all the continents were once joined in a supercontinent he called Pangaea, stretching from pole to pole. Wegener claimed that Pangaea had split into several pieces about 200 million years ago. The fragments started to move like icebergs, generally westward or, in some cases, toward the equator. For example, North America moved westward away from Eurasia and Africa to form the Atlantic Ocean. Wegener argued that mountains formed by compression and uplift as continents collided, and he attributed earthquakes and volcanic eruptions to continental drift.

To support his theory, he illustrated how the coastal outlines of continents such as Africa and South America correspond almost perfectly. He also noted that their mountain ranges run without interruption if viewed together, comparing this to matching fragments of a newspaper. As further proof, Wegener used measurements to demonstrate that Greenland was moving away from Europe. He also showed that there were similarities between the fossils, flora, and fauna of the continents.

After World War I, Wegener was denied a post as professor at a German university as a result of the controversy he had aroused. In 1924, he accepted an appointment in Austria at the University of Graz as a professor of meteorology and geophysics.

He led further expeditions to Greenland that departed in 1929 and 1930. On November 1, 1930, his fiftieth birthday, Wegener left a base in central Greenland and was never seen again.

DID YOU KNOW?

Wegener was at a loss to explain the underlying mechanism of his theory of continental drift, and it was discounted during his lifetime. By the 1950s, however, advances in the studies of oceanography and Earth's magnetism provided evidence for his theory. Gradually, scientists began to accept Wegener's theory, and the importance of his work finally received full recognition. Indeed, it led to the new discipline of plate tectonics—now a major principle of geology.

See *also*: EARTH • GEOLOGY • PLATE TECTONICS

Weightlessness

Astronauts on a space shuttle or in a space station achieve the age-old dream of flying without wings or machines to help them. They float around their cabins, apparently weightless, even though Earth's gravity still has them firmly in its grasp.

When the engines on a space rocket leaving Earth are switched off, the crew go in an instant from being squashed into their bunks to being suddenly weightless. They can float across the cabin with a gentle push. Objects that are not fastened down float past them. If they spill a drink, it floats around in drops. The crew and everything in the craft are said to be "weightless."

The word *weight* has two meanings. In one sense, it means the force acting on something because of gravity. However, astronauts are never free of gravity. For example, Earth's gravity at the altitude (height above Earth's surface) of the International Space Station (218 to 222 miles, or 351 to 358 kilometers) is only about 10 percent weaker than it is at the surface. In fact, it is Earth's strong gravitational pull that keeps the space station in orbit. Even the astronauts who traveled the much greater distance to the Moon on the Apollo missions were always being pulled by gravity—either the gravity of Earth or that of the Moon. So, in this sense of weight, astronauts are never weightless.

The second sense of weight refers to effects that follow from something being pulled by gravity. When a person sits on a chair, gravity pulls him or her down, but the chair prevents the person from falling. The person feels the chair pressing upward against his or her body. When the person stands up, he or she feels the floor pressing upward on his or her feet. Such feelings are what people normally call the feeling of weight, but these effects disappear if people start to fall freely.

▶ *Astronauts float in the weightless environment of space. Weightlessness is caused by free fall. Spacecraft in orbit around Earth are falling toward the planet with an acceleration equal to that of gravity.*

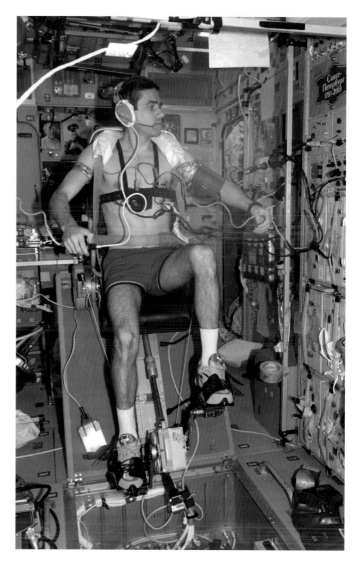

▲ *An astronaut trains on an exercise machine to combat the effects of the weightlessness. Astronauts experience health problems such as muscle and bone loss, blood changes, and motion sickness.*

For example, imagine a person standing in an elevator. The supporting cable breaks, and the brakes fail, so the elevator starts to fall down the elevator shaft freely. Everything in the cabin would fall at the same rate. (All objects fall at exactly the same rate under gravity, provided there is no air resistance, which slows them down by different amounts. In the closed cabin of the elevator, there is no air resistance.) The person standing in the elevator does not press down on the floor because the floor is dropping at the same speed as the person. Bags, hats, other people—all would float around inside the elevator.

This is exactly what happens in a spacecraft when the engines stop firing at the end of the launch. The craft immediately begins "falling." It travels more and more slowly. Everything inside the spacecraft does exactly the same thing because everything is affected in the same way by gravity. So the astronauts no longer press down on their chairs. Loose objects float around.

The space station is also "falling." If Earth's gravity could be switched off suddenly, the space station would hurtle off into space in a straight line. However, gravity is in fact constantly dragging it away from that straight line into an almost circular curved path around Earth. Again, everything on the space station is affected in the same way and so is traveling in almost the same orbit.

Things are different on a spacecraft when the engines are firing. The engines thrust the body of the ship forward, and the walls of the craft push the astronauts forward. They have feelings of "weight" that depend on how fast the engines are making the ship accelerate, rather than the strength of gravity at that point in space.

See also: FORCES • GRAVITY • MASS AND WEIGHT

Welding

Welding is the process used to join materials by melting their edges together. Many metal products, such as automobiles, are joined by welding. Plastics can also be welded. The heat for welding can be made by burning gases in a special torch. Other welding methods use beams of electrons or light from lasers.

Metals are the most common materials to be welded together, but the method is also used for other materials such as plastics. Welding was developed as a way of making swords, when strips of iron were heated and hammered together. Modern welding uses the sciences of metallurgy, physics, chemistry, and electronics.

Fusion and pressure
Most welds are made by fusion, when the edges of the materials melt with heat and then harden together. Many welds use a filler metal that also melts and fills the gap between the edges. There are also welds that use pressure rather than fusion or use a mixture of the two methods.

A fusion welding process needs a source of heat that can melt materials, such as steel. This heat may be from a flame or from an electric arc.

Gas welding
Some welding torches produce heat by burning gases such as acetylene with oxygen. Both gases are kept in steel cylinders and flow down hoses to the torch. The flame produced at the nozzle has a peak temperature of about 5400°F (3000°C).

Arc welding
An electric arc is a nonstop spark of electrical current that flows through the air between two contacts. If the piece of metal being worked is used

▲ Welding metals at extremely high temperatures produces light that is very intense and can damage the eyes. To protect the worker, a protective face mask, similar to a pair of sunglasses, is worn to filter the light. The mask also prevents sparks from landing on the welder's face and hair.

as one of the contacts, then an arc is created between the cathode of the welding torch and the workpiece—the anode.

The electric arc generates a great deal of heat and may have a temperature of between 27,000 and 36,000°F (15,000 to 20,000°C). To prevent the metal from burning away or oxidizing in the air, the arc is usually surrounded by a protective atmosphere of inert argon gas.

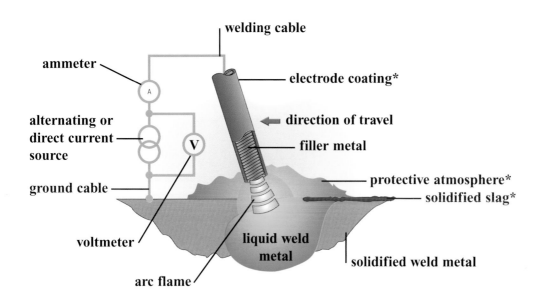

welding cable

ammeter

electrode coating*

alternating or
direct current
source

direction of travel

filler metal

ground cable

protective atmosphere*

solidified slag*

voltmeter

liquid weld
metal

solidified weld metal

arc flame

This illustration shows the method of arc welding with rod electrodes. Components marked with an asterisk are not present in some arc-welding processes.

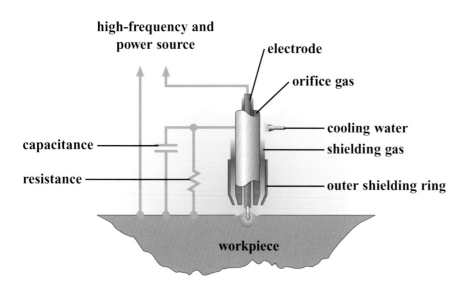

high-frequency and
power source

electrode

orifice gas

cooling water

capacitance

shielding gas

resistance

outer shielding ring

workpiece

This illustration shows the electric circuit for plasma/arc welding.

Manual arc welding

Manual metal arc welding is the most common arc-welding process. The electrode is a metal rod, which acts as a filler and is surrounded by a flux (a substance that promotes fusion). The rod is connected to the electrical supply. The welder briefly touches the rod against the work metal to start the arc.

The filler wire in the electrode melts and joins the edges of metal. The flux around the outside of the wire melts and helps keep the current flowing. The flux also shields the weld from the air to keep unwanted oxides (compounds of oxygen) and nitrides (compounds of nitrogen) from forming.

Plasma welding

In plasma welding, a nozzle is placed just beneath the electrode to make the arc narrower in size. By doing this, the speed of the gas increases, and the temperature of the arc is higher. The electrical power used in plasma welding is also greater than in conventional argon-gas welding.

The effect of the increased power and concentration on the workpiece being welded is to push a hole right through the metal. If the workpiece is moved past the torch, the keyhole moves along the line of the weld. The molten metal at the sides of the hole fills up the line as the torch moves along

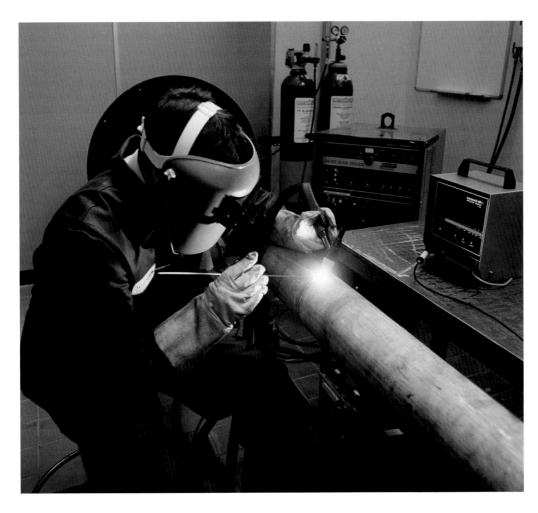

Some types of welding require the use of a flux material. The flux (the thin rod being held by the welder) is added to prevent oxide films from building up on the metals being joined. If the flux was not added, the oxides would cover the surfaces of the weld and stop the two halves from joining properly. This would make the joint weak and liable to fracture.

and produces a good weld. Plasma welding is more controllable than other arc welding methods and can be mechanized.

Electron-beam welding

This is a nonarc process that uses a beam of electrons similar to those inside a television tube. The system is in a chamber kept at a high vacuum (absence of air). The electrons are released by the negative cathode and are attracted to the anode, which is at a high positive voltage. The electrons pass through the anode at high speed and are then focused using electromagnets.

A fine beam of electrons at high power reaches the surface of the metal to be welded. The process produces a much greater keyhole effect than other methods. Narrow welds with a depth of 8 inches (20 centimeters) can be produced. A disadvantage is that the welding has to be carried out in a vacuum chamber.

Laser welding

The effect of a laser is to produce a beam of light or similar waves that contain concentrated pulses of energy. This energy can produce heat for welding. Early laser welds used a ruby laser, which produces a brief pulse of red light with a peak power of less than 100 megawatts. Ruby lasers are used for welding very small parts, which may be inside a glass vessel kept at a high vacuum.

A more recent development is the carbon dioxide laser, which produces a continuous beam of radiation. Output powers of 20 kilowatts are possible, although large power supplies are needed because the laser is only 10 percent efficient. The carbon dioxide gas of the laser must be kept cool, and large pumps and heat exchangers are also needed.

The wavelengths produced by the carbon dioxide laser are in the infrared region and cannot be seen. To make the main laser visible, an additional low-power laser with a red color is added.

A further problem is that most metals tend to reflect infrared wavelengths and act as a mirror for the laser. This problem is overcome when the laser is used at high power. The surface of the metal then begins to vaporize, the reflection drops, and the full power of the beam reaches the metal.

Carbon dioxide lasers are now used in factories to weld metal, such as on automobile parts. The laser can be beamed from hundreds of feet away if necessary and can weld thick steel quickly. In the future, these lasers may allow welding in difficult places, such as inside a nuclear reactor.

Resistance welding

This type of welding obtains heat for fusion from the electrical resistance at the joint between two materials, which have an electrode on either side. Pressure is used to make good contact at the places to be welded. Spot welding and seam welding are the most common types of resistance welding. The system is simple because no metal is lost, and no gases or fluxes are required. However, a large supply of electrical current is needed—up to 50,000 amps for heavy equipment.

Friction welding

In friction welding, the heat is produced by the rubbing of two surfaces under pressure. It is often used to weld the ends of tubes together. One tube is turned at high speed and then pressed onto the other tube. Great heat is generated, and, at the right moment, a joint is made.

Other types of welding processes

Explosion welding is similar to friction welding, but it happens more quickly. The heat for welding is produced by the impact between two surfaces.

Ultrasonic sound waves are also used for joining metals and plastics. The ultrahigh frequency sound waves produce small, rapid vibrations at the surfaces of the materials, and this causes enough frictional heat for welding.

▲ *Carbon dioxide laser welding is used in many industries to join thick pieces of steel. The process can be automated and controlled by an operator working in another room.*

See also: METAL • METALLURGY • PLASTIC

Wheel

Without the wheel, the growth of civilization might not have taken place. The wheel made the transportation of people and goods on land much faster and easier than before. As a result, people could then move from small, scattered villages along rivers and streams to large inland settlements. Food and supplies could be brought to the settlements using wheeled vehicles.

No one knows if the wagon wheel came before or after the potter's wheel. Because both were first made of wood, which rots quickly, there is no direct evidence left in most ancient sites. The potter's wheel can be dated by experts because pottery made on a wheel is clearly different from earlier pots and bowls. However, wagon wheels leave no traces once they have decomposed.

The oldest proof of the wagon wheel is a rough sketch on a clay tablet found in Mesopotamia (the fertile area that lies between the Tigris and Euphrates rivers in present-day Iraq), dating from from 3200–3100 BCE. These early wheels were made of three wooden planks held together with smaller pieces of wood fastened crosswise. The planks had been cut so that the natural knothole was in the center of the middle plank. This knothole was then used as the pivot.

Improving the wheel

One of the first improvements made to the wheel was to put a wooden rim around it, so the wear was even all the way around. Between four and five thousand years ago, the Mesopotamians studded

▶ *A waterwheel harnesses the power of flowing water to grind grain. The waterwheel in this picture is called an overshot wheel. Water flows into chambers, called buckets, on the wheel to turn it. The wheel then turns the grinding machinery of the mill.*

▲ **Alloy wheels not only look good, they also improve the handling of automobiles because they reduce the mass of the wheel and make steering much easier.**

the rim with copper nails to make the wheel last longer. These nails may even have held onto a tire made of thick leather.

The spoked wheel was the next big improvement. Spoked wheels are thought to have been developed by the Hittites of northern Syria or Anatolia. The spokes allowed bronze (an alloy of copper and tin) wheels to be cast, using far less metal than solid wheel designs. The spokes made the wheels much lighter and easier to move.

The next important change did not come for thousands of years, until the sixteenth century when wheels were designed to fit on tracks. This development led to the first passenger and freight railroad service, which opened in Britain around 1830. Toward the end of the same century, the invention of the bicycle, and then the automobile, led to the invention of the pneumatic (air-filled) tire to cover the wheel and make the ride smoother.

Modern developments

Early automobiles had wooden spoked wheels, wire wheels, or artillery wheels. By the 1930s, however, automobile wheels were being made of a highly popular material called pressed steel. Light aluminum or magnesium alloy wheels are now common, especially for sports cars.

See also: AUTOMOBILE • LOCOMOTIVE • RAILROAD SYSTEM

Winch and windlass

Winches, windlasses, and capstans are used to haul or lift heavy loads by a system of cables and ratchets. They are very ancient pieces of machinery, first developed by the Romans. They combine the principle of the lever with the wheel to move loads that are too heavy to be lifted by hand.

▲ *The maneuverability of modern yachts is aided by efficient windlasses that enable one person to hoist sails up and down with a minimum of effort, even in the roughest of weather conditions.*

The terms *winch* and *windlass* were once different words for the same device. A drum with a rope or cable wound around it is turned by a crank or other type of lever, and the rope pulls a load. These terms now have slightly different meanings. A windlass is a device turned by hand; a winch is one powered by a motor.

Multiplying the power

A simple windlass consists of a drum supported at each end and turned by a crank. In winches and windlasses, the cable drum is usually horizontal, but a capstan has a vertical cable drum. A force on the crank exerts a pull on a rope wound around the drum. The difference between the length of the crank and the drum diameter decides the amount of pull that will result from a given force on the crank. If the crank is much larger than the drum, the pull on the rope will be much larger than the force on the crank. This is the principle of the lever applied to a wheel.

A capstan works in the same way. If the capstan bars that a ship's crew pushes on are long, the force will be much greater than if they are short.

Of course, a crank cannot be too large because it would be impossible to reach it at the top of its turn. The Romans solved this problem with men turning a huge wheel by walking around inside it. Later, the crank turned a shaft with a small gear wheel on it. This small gear wheel turned a larger gear wheel on the same shaft as the cable drum. A certain number of turns of the crank were needed to turn the cable drum once. This reduced the force needed to pull a heavy weight on the end of the rope. Running the rope through a system of pulleys also meant that a small force on the crank produced a powerful pull on the load.

The differential windlass

The Chinese (differential) windlass works in another way. Two cable drums of different diameters are mounted on the same shaft so they turn together. The cable is wound on the drums in such a way that as it unwinds from one drum, it is being wound up on the other. To pull the load, the shaft is turned so that the rope is wound off the smaller drum and onto the larger one.

The closer the two drums are in size, the smaller the distance the load is moved for one turn on the shaft. Also, less force is needed to move the load through a smaller distance.

Modern types of winches

Most winches are now made of steel. They are fitted with a ratchet mechanism that keeps the cable drum from turning the wrong way, so the load cannot pull the cable drum around unexpectedly. When the load has to be lowered, a brake slows the

HOISTING WINCH

ratchet mechanism behind plate

shaft for winding winch the other way

handle can be removed and put on the other shaft

brake lever

cable drum

band brake

steel plate frame

YACHT WINDLASS

warping end

upper spindle drives warping end with or without cable wheel

ratchet

foot brake lever

lower spindle drives cable wheel with or without warping end

band brake

cable wheel

drum down to a safe speed. This brake is usually a band brake, which works by tightening a flexible steel band around the drum to increase the friction.

Some cable drums and nearly all capstans are mounted with one end free. This is important because it means that a loop of rope can be slipped over it. In this way, any rope can be looped around the capstan a few times and pulled tight, creating enough friction between the capstan and the rope to pull the load. One capstan can be used to hoist several different sails.

Power-driven capstans

In a power-driven capstan, the motor is set to turn the capstan continuously, and the rope is looped around it loosely. When the load is attached to the other end, the capstan operator tightens the loop by pulling on the loose end of the rope. The capstan pulls on the rope, and when the load has been pulled far enough, the operator loosens the rope a little so the capstan slips in the loop. This is an easy and flexible way of working the machine. Where the cable drum is held at both ends, a single rope is permanently attached to the drum. The most common use of the capstan is for hoisting the anchor of a ship.

▲ *The hoisting winch (left) has a ratchet to stop the drum from slipping backward and a brake to slow it when lowering heavy loads. The larger yacht windlass (right) is used for hoisting large sails. The warping end is used to haul any rope by wrapping the cable around it a few times and keeping the loose end taught.*

▼ *The power-driven winch on a ship allows heavy loads to be pulled without any physical effort by the crew.*

See also: LEVER • PULLEY

Wind

Winds are the constant movements of air that help control world climates by carrying heat from the tropics toward the poles. Winds keep the tropics from becoming too hot and the midlatitudes from becoming too cold. Winds also bring moisture from the sea to the land.

Most of the air and water vapor in the atmosphere is found in the lowest level, called the troposphere. The upper boundary of the troposphere is called the tropopause. The tropopause varies in height between the equator and the poles. It is about 11 miles (18 kilometers) above Earth's surface at the equator but only about 5 miles (8 kilometers) above Earth's surface at the poles. The air in it is constantly moving because of the unequal heating of Earth's surface by the Sun. The atmosphere is similar to a vast heat-exchange system powered by the Sun. The moving air ensures that heat is exchanged between the tropics and the poles.

Circulation of the atmosphere

Sunlight passes through the atmosphere and heats Earth's surface. At the equator, where the Sun's rays are most intense, heat from the surface warms the air. As the air warms, it expands and rises to create a region of low air pressure near the surface, where winds are light. This region is called the doldrums.

Gradually, the rising air cools and spreads out. Some of the air flows north and some flows south. Around latitudes 30 degrees North and 30 degrees South, this air sinks back to the surface. The sinking air creates high air pressure systems at the surface. These are called the horse latitudes.

▶ *Strong winds blow palm trees in the Caribbean in the buildup to a hurricane. Hurricane-force winds blow at 74 miles (120 kilometers) per hour or more, causing widespread damage to the affected area.*

The horse latitudes are regions of dry, warm, sinking air. Over the land, they are desert zones. The sinking air moves outward from the horse latitudes. Some flows back toward the doldrums, and some flows toward the poles. The air that flows from the horse latitudes back across the surface toward the equator forms the trade winds. These winds do not flow in a straight north-south line. Because Earth is spinning on its axis, all winds are deflected to the right of their natural direction in the Northern Hemisphere; and to the left, in the Southern Hemisphere. This is called the Coriolis effect, named for French mathematician Gaspard-Gustave de Coriolis (1792–1843) who described the effect in 1835. Hence, the trade winds in the Northern Hemisphere blow from the northeast to the southwest, not from north to south. They are the northeast trade winds. (Winds are always

◄ *Glider pilots use the wind to stay airborne. Thermals are columns of rising air created by the Sun heating Earth's surface. Ridge lift is created when winds blow against mountains or hills. Wave lift occurs on the leeward side of the peak when wind blows over the mountain rather than up one side.*

named for the direction from which they blow.) In the Southern Hemisphere, the southeast trade winds blow from the southeast to the northwest.

The air that flows poleward from the horse latitudes forms the westerlies. In the Northern Hemisphere, they blow from the southwest to the northeast. In the Southern Hemisphere, they blow from the northwest to the southeast. The westerlies are warm winds. They eventually meet up with cold winds coming from the poles, where dense air is sinking. These cold winds are called the polar easterlies. The boundary between the polar easterlies and the westerlies is called the polar front.

The trade winds, the westerlies, and the polar easterlies are the prevailing (main) winds in any region. However, wind belts move north and south throughout the year because Earth's axis is tilted. Monsoon winds change direction according to season. In winter, for example, there is a high air pressure system over southern Asia, from which flow the dry northeast trade winds. In summer, intense heating of the land creates a low air pressure system over the land. The southeast trade winds are drawn across the equator and toward the land as southwesterly winds. These monsoon winds are warm and moist, and they bring heavy rain to the

▶ *This map shows the direction and location of the major winds around the world.*

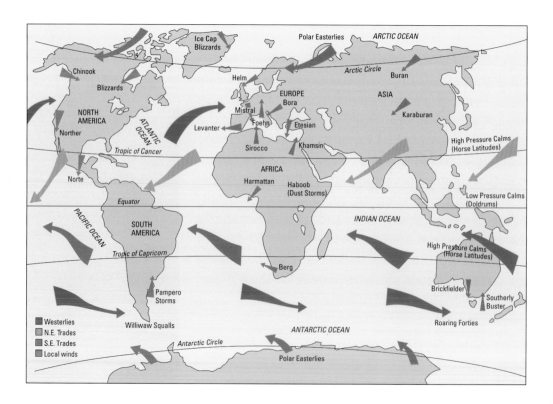

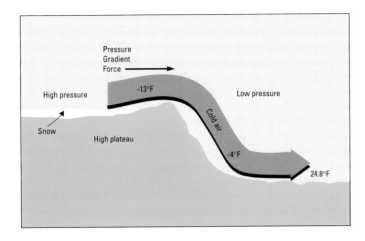

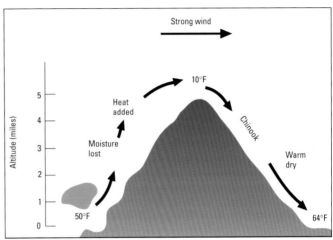

◀ *Katabatic winds form where cold air rushes downhill from an elevated frozen plateau.*

▼ *When precipitation falls on the windward side of a mountain, it can enhance a chinook by making the downward air warmer and drier.*

Indian subcontinent. Changeable winds are also a feature of the midlatitudes, especially in depressions (rotating low air pressure systems). Other variations are caused by the shape of the land.

Local winds

Land and sea breezes occur because the land heats up and cools down at a faster rate than does the sea. During the day, the land heats up quickly. Hot air rises, and cool air from the sea flows in to replace it. At night, the land cools rapidly. The air over the land then becomes cooler than the air over the sea, so air flows from the land to the sea.

Anabatic and katabatic winds are caused in a similar way. Anabatic winds are warm and flow up mountain slopes during the day. Katabatic winds occur at night, when cold, dense air from high slopes flows downward into valleys (see the illustration above left).

BEAUFORT WIND SCALE

Beaufort number	Speed (miles per hour)	Speed (kilometers per hour)	Description
0	< 1	< 1	Calm
1	1–3	1–5	Light air
2	4–7	6–11	Slight breeze
3	8–12	12–19	Gentle breeze
4	13–18	20–28	Moderate breeze
5	19–24	29–38	Fresh breeze
6	25–31	39–49	Strong breeze
7	32–38	50–61	Moderate gale
8	39–46	62–74	Gale
9	47–54	75–88	Strong gale
10	55–63	89–102	Whole gale
11	64–73	103–117	Storm
12	≥ 74	≥ 118	Hurricane

▲ *A wind tunnel is used to test the aerodynamics of an automobile to discover the effects upon it of air in motion. The wind tunnel must provide a flow of air or gas that is steady and smooth and that can be controlled and measured precisely.*

Well-known local winds are caused by special factors. For example, the chinook in North America is a warm wind that melts the snow on the leeward slopes of the Rocky Mountains. This wind has been known to raise temperatures by 30 to 40°F (17 to 22°C) in an hour or so.

Dangerous winds

Microbursts are intense downward surges of cool air that come from rain clouds. They produce strong, changing wind patterns, called wind shear, that are especially dangerous for airplanes taking off and landing. The plane first meets a headwind, which lifts the airplane's nose. An abrupt shift to a tailwind causes the plane to fall, nose first, often too fast for the pilot to keep the plane under control.

Scientists are working on ways to detect oncoming microbursts so that pilots can be warned in time. In the meantime, pilots are being trained to recognize microbursts and to handle wind shear when they meet it.

Wind speeds vary greatly. They are measured on the Beaufort scale, where 0 represents calm air, and 12 represents a hurricane-force wind. Winds reach their greatest speeds when the pressure gradient is steep. The pressure gradient is the rate at which the air pressure changes across Earth's surface. On weather maps, steep pressure gradients occur when isobars (lines joining places with equal air pressure) are close together. The pressure gradient is gentle when the isobars are widely spaced.

Jet streams

The speed of winds that blow over Earth's surface is reduced by friction and by land barriers, such as mountains. No such factors restrict wind speeds in the upper air. In the midlatitudes, around the tropopause, there are fast winds called jet streams. Jet streams are broad bands of fast-moving air, up to 100 miles (160 kilometers) wide and 1 mile (1.6 kilometers) deep. They can travel at speeds of up to 300 miles (485 kilometers) per hour. Pilots avoid flying into these powerful winds, but they are happy to use them as tailwinds. The jet stream flows in a westerly direction across the United States, often looping north and south. Jet streams are strongest in winter, when temperature differences between the polar and tropical regions are greatest, and the pressure gradient between these regions in the upper air is at its most steep.

See also: AIR • WEATHER SYSTEM

Windmill and wind pump

Wind power is free. It can be used anywhere in the world to drive a mill for grinding grain into flour, to pump water out of low-lying land or a shallow aquifer, or to power simple machinery. Wind power is now being used to run generators and produce cheap electricity.

Until the invention of the steam engine, wind was one of only three sources of power. The other two were water, which needed a river, and people or animals, both of whom had to be persuaded to work by rewards. On the other hand, wind could be put to work anywhere, and it cost nothing in salary or animal feed.

The first windmill in Europe appeared in 1150. The design was probably brought back from the Middle East. This early windmill was a small wooden building with a gabled (triangular) roof, supported on a thick, wooden post. The post was held in place by ties and crossbeams, and it had an iron bearing at the upper end. A framework of four crossed wooden sticks was covered with cloth and set into a groove in the post. This sail turned in the wind and drove a millstone by means of a gearing (a device that passes motion from one part of a machine to another) in a wooden wheel. The windmill revolved and could be turned into the wind no matter from where the wind was coming. Such windmills were used for pumping water and driving sawmills as well as grinding grain.

Milling grain was heavy work. The grain was put between two large, circular flat stones, one of which was then turned. The grain was crushed and scraped, and the flour came out around the edge.

▶ *These tower windmills have a cap that can be rotated to catch the wind. The miller does this by moving the post (the long diagonal timber leading down from the cap) until the sails begin to turn again.*

Basic structure

A windmill consists of several important elements. First there are sails, which are pushed around by the wind. They are attached to a large windshaft set nearly horizontal, which also carries a brake wheel.

A vertical shaft carries the power from the windshaft to the millstones. The power comes from the windshaft by way of a small gearwheel, called the wallower, attached to the vertical shaft. The wallower is driven by the brake wheel on the windshaft and so turns the vertical shaft. The vertical shaft then drives the millstones.

Finally, part of the structure supporting the mechanism must be able to turn around so that the sails will point straight into the wind. There are two ways of turning the structure, and they give their names to the two types of windmills.

▲ *The windmill's sails turn a horizontal shaft (the large shaft at center left) that is connected to a brake wheel. The brake wheel connects with a horizontal wallower. The millstones are situated at the bottom of the vertical shaft.*

The post mill

Post mills were the earliest type of windmill. An upright post was supported on a timber base and kept steady by quarter bars running between the post and the base at an angle of 30 degrees. The mill was balanced on this post, similar to an upturned glass on a vertical pencil.

It was easy to move the mill around. For one thing, the structure was built of wood and was therefore light. It had a tail pole, which was a long pole projecting out on the opposite side of the sails. This pole normally rested on the ground. When the wind changed direction, and the miller wanted to turn the mill into the wind, the miller would pick up the end of the pole and move it until the sails were facing into the wind again.

Later, the tail pole often included a stairway leading up into the mill. In this type of mill, the lower end generally had wheels so that the miller did not have to lift the weight of the stairs when turning the mill.

One disadvantage of the post mills was that the light structure was easily damaged during storms, and sometimes they were even blown down. Fire was also a risk in a wooden building. The timber was also liable to rot. The upper structure could be replaced in parts as needed. If the base or quarter bars rotted, however, the entire mill would have to be taken apart to be repaired.

To avoid this problem, post mills were later built on a stone or brick base, which could also be used as a storehouse.

The tower mill

The tower mill was probably invented to be a more solid structure than the post mill. The tower was a tall brick or stone building housing the millstones and the vertical shaft. On top was set a cap of timber, which carried the windshaft. This cap was the only part of the mill that was free to turn into the wind. To do this, it was mounted on wheels running on a circular track around the top of the tower. Other wheels ran around against the inside of the tower to keep the cap from coming off its rails. As a result, only the cap was in danger of being destroyed during a storm. The sturdy tower could also survive fire, rot, and even floods.

The sails

A windmill's sails were originally just that—canvas spread out on the arms to catch the wind. Strips of canvas were attached to a light framework on the arms, called sail stock. The canvas was fixed at an angle to each arm, similar to the blades of a propeller, so the wind would push against them and rotate the arms.

It took a long time for the miller to climb up each arm and set the canvas each time the mill was needed. Strong wind could split the canvas, which would also rot after a while. To overcome these problems, a system of hinged wooden shutters was invented to act as sails. They were all linked together by rods and were kept in the set position by a strong spring. If the wind became too strong, the shutters would open against the spring and allow the wind to spill out, so reducing the speed. This system of spring sails was invented by Scottish millwright Andrew Meickle in 1772.

Later still, the angle of the shutters could be adjusted from inside the mill by a system of rods and pulleys.

The milling machinery

Grain was milled between two heavy stones, one of which was fixed in place while the other turned. The grain was held in a hopper (large bin) and fed into the gap between the stones near their centers.

The milling surfaces of the stones were not smooth. A precise pattern of grooves had to be cut in them, so the grain was scraped from the center of the round stones toward the edges, where the milled grain was collected as flour in a trough. Cutting this pattern with a hammer and chisel was an extremely skilled job.

Some mills had only one set of millstones. Others had two sets, both working off the same vertical shaft and spur wheel. Millstones were extremely heavy, often weighing several hundred pounds each. They were usually made of granite.

The miller also used wind power to run other pieces of machinery. For example, a hoist for lifting sacks of grain up into the bin over the millstones was powered from the windshaft. A simple clutch, similar to that in a modern automobile, was operated when the hoist was needed.

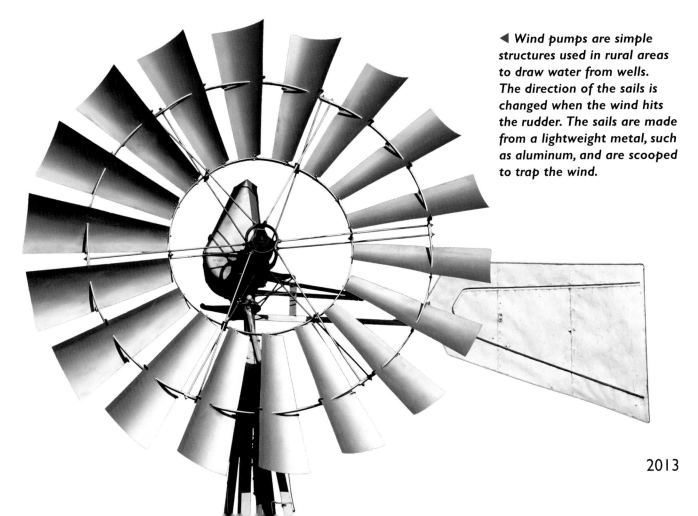

◀ *Wind pumps are simple structures used in rural areas to draw water from wells. The direction of the sails is changed when the wind hits the rudder. The sails are made from a lightweight metal, such as aluminum, and are scooped to trap the wind.*

◄ *Large wind turbines are a common feature in many parts of the United States. The propellers turn a shaft that is connected to a generator at the bottom of the structure. The generator produces electricity that can be fed into the local grid.*

The fantail

A miller might have to turn the mill dozens of times a day to keep the sails facing into the wind. As a result, a device called a fantail was invented to do the job instead. The fantail was a tiny windmill mounted on the side opposite the big sails. (On a post mill, the fantail was set on the end of the tail pole.) The fantail was fixed vertically but at right angles to the sails. When the sails were facing directly into the wind, the fantail was parallel to the airflow so it did not turn.

If the wind shifted direction, it would begin to turn the fantail. This would turn a shaft running from the fantail down to wheels or a worm gear, which would turn the mill back into the wind. When the sails were once more facing into the wind—and the fantail was therefore parallel to it—the wind would stop turning the fantail, and the mill would stop in its new position.

Other uses for a windmill

Windmills were used as a source of power for pumping water from low-lying land in the Netherlands and parts of southeastern England. Much good land was thereby reclaimed for farming. Wind power was also used to press oil from seeds and for sawing wood and stone. In parts of the West Indies, windmills were used to crush sugarcane. Sugar mills can still be seen in Barbados.

Modern wind-powered machines

Wind power is still used in some parts of the world to raise water from wells for use in the home or in agriculture. The modern wind pump works like the older windmills, with metal sails driving a pump through a shaft. It has a fixed tail (rudder) in place of the fantail to keep the sails facing into the wind. The tail is spring-loaded, so when the wind becomes too strong, the sails are pointed at an angle to the wind. The pump is started and stopped by a mechanism that changes the angle of the tail.

Experiments have been going on for many years to generate electricity using wind power. Large wind turbines have been tried, including some unusual designs. One device uses a pair of sails turning on a vertical axis, so it never needs to be moved to face into the wind. An increasing number of wind farms are being set up in hilly areas to exploit this renewable energy resource.

See also: PUMP • WIND

Wire and cable

Wire is made by pulling rods made of metal through holes in a mold. The drawn metal can then be made into many different shapes and sizes.

Wire has hundreds of uses—from needles and pins made from short pieces of single wire to cables made from twisting many wire strands together. Gold, silver, and bronze wires have been found in the ruins of Troy and in ancient Egyptian tombs. From these early times up to the fourteenth century, wire was made either by cutting thin strips from metal sheets or, in Roman times, by heating iron bars and beating them down to the required thickness on an anvil.

Wire drawing, where metal rods are pulled through a hole in a die (mold), was used to make wire from the fourteenth century in Germany. Until the nineteenth century, wire drawing was done by hand and relied on the strength of the person pulling the wire through the die.

Preparing the metal

The metal rods, usually steel or copper, are made by passing hot strips of metal through rollers. Oxygen in the air causes a coating of scale to form on the hot surface of the rods, and this must be removed before they can be drawn. The scale is removed by the pickling process, in which the rods are placed in baths of sulfuric acid (H_2SO_4) or hydrochloric acid (HCl) and water. The mixture of acid and water loosens the scale, which is then washed away by powerful jets of water. Scale may also be removed by blasting the rods with abrasives. After pickling, the rods are washed in limewater (a solution of calcium hydroxide; $Ca(OH)_2$) to remove any acid.

The rods are next coated with a material that will help lubricate (grease) the rod or that will help a lubricant to stick to the rod as it is drawn through the die. The kind of lubricating coating depends on

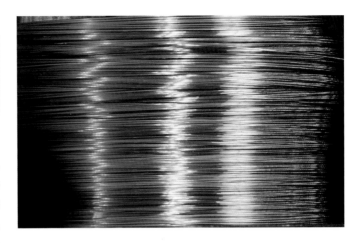

▲ Coils of metal wire start out as thin rods of metal. It may take several passes through a die plate of progressively smaller diameters before the wire is drawn into the required thickness.

▲ The wire may have to be reheated (below) to soften it before it is drawn to the required size.

enters the die to the narrower diameter of the wire that leaves the die. The wire can be made thinner by passing it through narrower and narrower dies until the correct size is reached. Unlike the rods, which are formed from hot metal, wire is always cold when drawn through the dies. Lubricants are always used when metal is drawn through a die. They can be either wet, such as oils and soaps, or dry, such as greases and soap powders.

Wire drawing

To make very long lengths of wire, long metal rods are welded together, end to end. When wire is to be drawn, the end of the metal rod is sharpened to a point and threaded through the die. It is gripped at the other end of the die and fastened to a drawing block. An electric motor turns the drawing block, which quickly pulls the rod through the die, making it thinner and longer. The die hole is slightly smaller than the diameter of the finished wire because the metal will swell slightly after the wire leaves the die.

Because wire can be reduced in thickness only gradually, it may have to go through several dies before the correct thinness is reached. Each pass through the die (called a draft) hardens the wire, so that if several drafts are needed, the wire may have to be heated to soften it. Modern machines can

▲ *Wire-making machines can produce a large number of strands at a time. Machine-made wires pass through a number of drafts in one operation and can be made in longer lengths than hand-drawn wires.*

the kind of metal rod used and the purpose of the finished wire. Some metal rods are given a coating of brown iron oxide (Fe_2O_3) and baked. Wire used for some kinds of springs is dipped in liquid metal, often copper sulfate ($CuSO_4$).

The die

There are many kinds of dies, the simplest being a draw plate. This plate is made of a hard material, which at one time was steel. Modern draw plates and dies are made from materials such as tungsten carbide (WC) for larger-sized wires and diamond for thin wires. The draw plate has a number of holes that taper from the thickness of the rod that

▶ *These metal bars are the first stage in the wire-forming process. They are rolled into rods and stripped of any scale by pickling in acid. The rods are then coated in grease to help them pass through the die.*

▶ *Strong wire cables are used to support the roadway of a bridge. The strength of the cables comes from the many individual strands of wire that are twisted together into cables and then twisted again into a much thicker single cable.*

draw a wire through all the drafts needed to reduce its thickness in a single operation. As each draft increases the length of the wire, however, each drawing block must turn at a faster speed than the one before it.

Some uses for wire

There are many kinds of wire for many different uses, including galvanized wire that will not rust, wire mesh for fencing and caging, and barbed wire for fencing. Not all wire is for use in long sections. Needles and pins, for example, are made from long lengths of wire, as are steel rivets.

Wire that will become needles and pins is first straightened by being guided through rollers. The wire is then gripped and, if pins are to be made, the end is struck by a header die, which forms the pin head. A cutter chops the wire one pin's length from the head, and this end is sharpened by files or cutters. If needles are to be made, a length of the straightened wire the size of two needles is cut. Both ends are sharpened on a grinding machine. Next, the wire is fed into a machine that stamps two eyes in the center. The metal in the center of each eye is then punched out, the wire strip is broken into two needles, and the waste metal around the eye ends is ground off.

The needles are then hardened in hot oil at 1472°F (800°C) and tempered in furnaces at 392°F (200°C). Emery and soft soap are used to scour away any grinding marks or scale left from the heat treatment. All needles are nickel plated by electrolysis, and sometimes the eyes are gilded (gold plated).

Cables or wire ropes

Wire can be strengthened for some uses—such as holding up bridges or mooring ships in harbors—by stranding and weaving many wires together into wire ropes called cables.

No one knows when cables were first used, but part of a bronze wire cable was found in the ruins of Pompeii, in Italy, which was destroyed by a volcanic eruption in 79 CE. Modern cable manufacture began around 1870, using iron wires instead of the steel that is used today.

Making cables

Just as rope is made by twisting fibers of hemp, sisal, manila, or other material together, so wire rope is made by first twisting a number of wires together in a spiral to make a strand. Sometimes these are twisted around a core (center) of plant fiber or wire. Several strands are then twisted together to form a cable. The strands may also be twisted around a core of sisal to make the cable easier to bend.

Cables are made by machines. Those that make smaller-sized cables can be small enough to fit onto a bench. Others may be as big as a one-story house. Several bobbins (reels) of wire strands or single wires are led through guide holes to the front of the

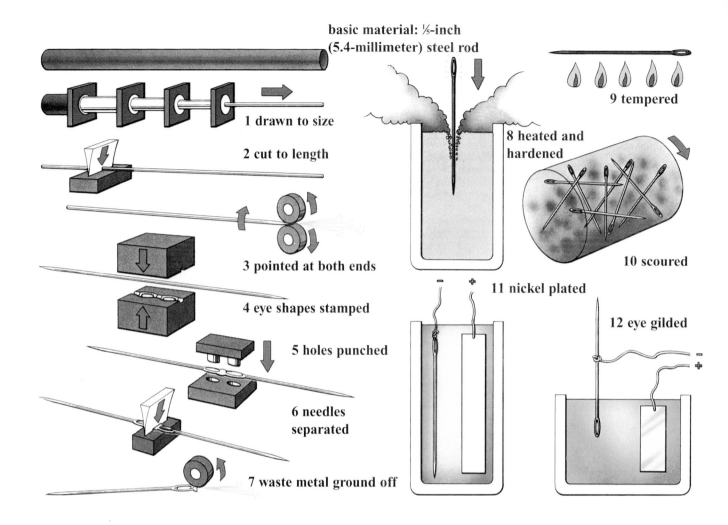

basic material: ⅕-inch
(5.4-millimeter) steel rod

1 drawn to size

2 cut to length

3 pointed at both ends

4 eye shapes stamped

5 holes punched

6 needles
separated

7 waste metal ground off

8 heated and
hardened

9 tempered

10 scoured

11 nickel plated

12 eye gilded

▲ *This diagram shows the twelve stages involved in making a needle. The process starts using a steel rod, which is drawn, stamped, and sharpened. The needle is finished by coating the shaft of the needle with nickel and the eye of the needle with gold.*

machine, where they are twisted together. The outer section of the machine, with its bobbins fixed, spins around and produces a twisted wire rope or strand in front. This is lubricated, pulled from the machine, and fed into a die, which straightens any slight bends or wrong twists in any of the wires.

Cables can be twisted in more than one pattern. The two most widely used ways to lay (twist) ropes are the regular lay and the Lang lay. When making regular lay ropes, the finished spiral twist of the rope is in the opposite direction from the spiral twist of the strands. In the Lang lay ropes, the finished spiral twist of the rope is in the same direction as that of the twist in the strands.

Each type of cable is labeled by two numbers—the first number shows the number of strands in the cable, and the second number shows the number of wires in each strand. Cables are usually made according to four number designs: 6:7 cable

is used for heavy pulling jobs; 6:19 is most often used for hoisting; 6:37 is a very pliable cable for smaller hoisting jobs; and 8:19, which can be used in place of 6:37, although it can lose its shape and would not be used where cables are liable to be crushed.

Although the core of a cable is greased and the strands lubricated while it is being made, this protection will not last for the lifetime of the cable. Cables must be kept clean and occasionally regreased with a petroleum jelly.

See also: METAL • WELDING

Woodworking

People have made objects out of wood for thousands of years. Wood still has many different uses inside and outside the home. Simple tools, such as hand saws, are used to cut and shape wood. Modern machines are faster and more accurate than the best woodworker.

Wood is a natural and versatile material that has many uses, ranging from construction to practical and ornamental items such as furniture and decorative pieces. When wood arrives from the lumber mill, it has already had its bark stripped and has been cut into planks of various thicknesses. Depending on its purpose, the wood can then be worked into different shapes and finishes using a variety of machine tools.

The lathe

Wood is made into rounded shapes, such as chair legs, on a lathe. The wood is spun around on a horizontal axis against a fixed cutting tool, which shapes it. For centuries, it took two people to work a lathe—one to hold the cutting tool and one to crank around the spindle holding the wood.

An early way of turning the wood was to wrap a cord around the wood and pull the cord with a foot pedal. A tree branch at the other end of the cord would pull it back. Italian artist, inventor, and scientist Leonardo da Vinci (1452–1519) is credited with inventing the first lathe needing only one operator to work smoothly. Electric motors are now used to drive lathes.

Circular saws

The common type of motorized saw is the circular saw, also called a table saw. This saw has a blade made from a disk of steel with sharp teeth around its edge. The saw blade is turned on its shaft and cuts through a slot from underneath a table.

The height of the table can be changed so that the blade can cut to different depths. On some saws, the table or the blade can be tilted to make cuts on a slant—called bevel, or miter, cuts. If two boards are each sawed at an angle of 45 degrees, they will make a 90-degree turn without showing any grain.

◀ *A lathe is used for creating round or cylindrical shapes from pieces of wood. The wood is clamped at both ends and turned by a motor. By holding a sharp tool against the wood as it turns, the carpenter can cut decorative curves.*

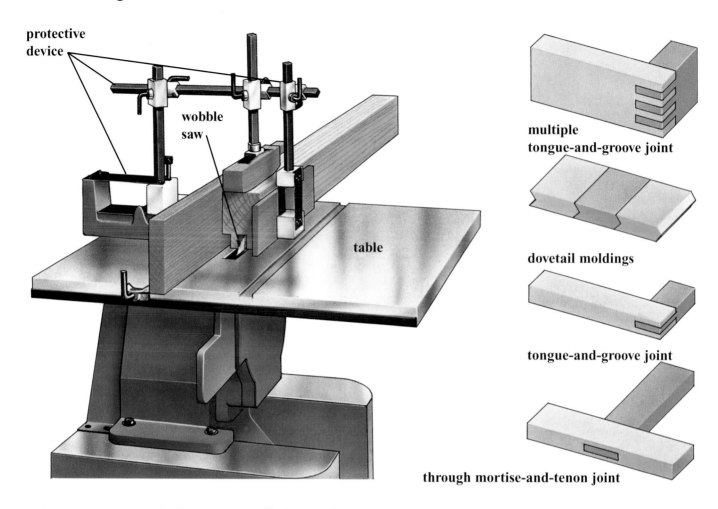

protective device

wobble saw

table

multiple tongue-and-groove joint

dovetail moldings

tongue-and-groove joint

through mortise-and-tenon joint

A common type of table saw has a blade 8 inches (20 centimeters) across, but blades can be as large as 16 inches (40 centimeters). When the teeth get blunt from use, they can be sharpened with a file.

Radial saws

The radial-arm saw is a type of circular saw in which the motor and the blade hang from an arm over the table. The arm moves in a full circle and can be clamped in any position over the wood. The motor and the blade can also be turned in a circle, or tilted to one side.

For some cuts, the wood is held on the table, and the radial arm is moved toward or away from the operator. If the wood is to be rip cut, with the grain, then the arm is clamped tightly and lumber is pushed into the blade.

▶ Portable circular saws can be used by do-it-yourself enthusiasts to cut large pieces of wood to size. The saw blade is covered by a protective hood to prevent accidents from occurring.

▲ This illustration shows a table saw with the devices for holding the wood steady. The wobble attachment cuts grooves in the wood. Other attachments can make cuts in two pieces of wood at once to give the accurate joints shown on the right.

◀ *Sanding wooden objects after they have been made gives them a smooth surface, which can then be varnished or painted.*

Band saws and jigsaws

The band saw has a blade made from a strip of metal with teeth, which runs on two large wheels, top and bottom, and passes through a slot in the worktable. The band saw can cut curves and patterns in thick wood or thin slices from the edges of boards. Band saws in sawmills can have teeth on both edges so that, when a log is passed back and forth, a board can be cut from it in each direction.

Similar to the band saw, the blade of the jigsaw passes through a hole in the table, but the blade moves up and down on a frame driven by the motor. Jigsaws are used to make curving cuts.

Circular saws and jigsaws are also made in smaller portable models to be used in the home for do-it-yourself projects. The worktable in this case is often the piece of wood itself, resting on supports called sawhorses.

Planers

The planer is used to make pieces of wood of even thicknesses by shaving thin layers from the surfaces. On the adjustable table there is a cutter head holding three or more knives.

There are planers for different sizes of wood between 18 and 50 inches (45 and 130 centimeters). Some industrial planers can smooth all four sides of a board at one time.

Jointers

The jointer works in a similar way to the planer in that it shaves off a layer of wood to form part of a joint. The jointer uses two tables—the front table feeds the wood into the cutting knife, and the back table receives the wood that has been cut. The size of the cut depends on the height of the front table. The cutter knives vary in length from 6 to 24 inches (20 to 85 centimeters) in length.

Shapers and routers

The shaper is used to cut curved and fancy edges on, for example, tabletops and picture frames. The cutter blades are adjusted to give the desired shape. These blades turn on a spindle and poke through a table that carries the wood to be shaped.

The router is a type of shaper turned upside down, with the spindle hanging over the table. It is used for shaping the insides of wooden bowls, the backs of chairs, and similar work.

Mortiser

A mortise is a slot with square corners. A tenon is a projection with square corners that fits into the mortise to make a mortise-and-tenon joint. A tongue-and-groove joint is similar, but the groove is open and easier to cut. The mortiser is a square-shaped hollow chisel with a boring tool inside.

◄ *Woodworking classes are an ideal way to learn basic carpentry skills, such as cutting, shaping, jointing, and smoothing wooden objects.*

First, it drills a hole almost as large as the shape wanted. The chisel then removes the corners. This tool can be mounted flat or vertically.

Drilling machines

Many people have a portable electric drill for doing jobs around the home, but a high degree of accuracy is needed for drilling holes in industry. A drill press or boring tool has the drill permanently fixed on an arm above a table. The wood is clamped on the table, and the drill is lowered onto it. The boring tools used in modern mass production often contain several drills that bore more than one hole at a time. The drilling head may be able to move around the piece of wood being worked and can be guided by computer.

Sanders

When shaping is finished, the wood surface is smoothed by a sander—a machine equipped with a disk or belt covered with sandpaper. Either the wood is pressed gently against the spinning disk or moving belt, or the sander is moved over the surface of the wood as it is held in place.

Some machines have sandpaper-covered spindles for smoothing more intricately shaped wood pieces. As the name suggests, drum sanders are revolving drums covered with sandpaper. They are used to smooth panels and flat pieces. A simple rotary sander is a disk of sandpaper and may leave swirl marks on the wood. Orbital sanders have a rectangular plate that moves back and forth as it turns so that it does not leave swirl marks. Users of sanders are advised to wear masks to protect them from the fine dust produced during sanding.

Multipurpose tools

Some machines can perform more than one type of task when they are equipped with different attachments. For example, a portable drill may be converted to a sander, a planer, or even a saw with the right parts. Many tools used for projects at home no longer need to be connected to a power supply. Instead, they have a rechargeable battery that enables them to be used for long periods in difficult or remote locations.

For the highest-quality work, such as furniture manufacture or veneer cutting, factories need specialized machines. Large-scale production also needs machines that can work for long periods at high speed.

See also: DRILL • TIMBER INDUSTRY

Wool

Wool is a fiber that comes from sheep and other animals. It is used mainly for weaving or knitting fabric. Wool is especially useful for making clothes and blankets for people who live in cold countries because it is good at keeping in body heat.

Wool is a natural material that comes from the coat of a hairy animal. The hair is cut from the animal's body and spun into yarn, from which cloth can be made. All mammals, including humans, have hair covering their bodies, but only a few have hair suitable for use as wool. These include camels, goats, llamas, alpacas, and even rabbits, as well as sheep—the most widely used.

Sheep's wool has been used for centuries as a fiber from which to make warm clothes. It is a good insulator, trapping heat close to the body for warmth in cold weather. It can absorb moisture, so perspiration does not make it uncomfortable to wear wool. It is very durable and can be used to make upholstery and carpets as well as clothes.

Similar to other animal hair, wool is a protein called keratin, of which animal horns and hooves, as well as fingernails and toenails, are made. In the case of wool and other forms of hair, the keratin forms a fiber. These fibers are cylindrical in shape, with overlapping scales on the surface. These scales help the strands of fiber lock together in a process called felting. Felt itself is made from wool fibers that have been pressed together.

The history of wool production

People have been spinning wool into thread to make clothes since about 4000 BCE in central Asia. Trade in wool grew many centuries ago among the countries that surround the Mediterranean Sea. A particular kind of sheep—the Merino, which produces especially fine wool—was bred in Spain

▲ *The origins of hand knitting are unknown, but knitted woolen socks have been found in Egyptian tombs dating from the third century CE. Knitting was a key part of the textile industry in medieval Europe.*

from about 100 CE. From that time, and for many hundreds of years onward, Spain was one of Europe's largest wool producers. Britain, too, was a producer of large quantities of wool.

Throughout Europe, people kept sheep and spun their own wool to weave into cloth. A variety of different kinds of sheep were bred to suit the climate and conditions of the different areas in which they lived. Many still exist—the Corriedale, for example, raised originally in New Zealand, produces wool used for rugged clothing.

Merino sheep were introduced into Australia in the eighteenth century, and they were so successful that Australia became the world's leading producer of Merino wool. The Spanish brought the first sheep to what is now the United States in the sixteenth century, and they sold the first Merino sheep to Americans in the eighteenth century.

From farm to factory

Wool is produced all over the world. China is the second largest producer of raw wool after Australia. Although almost every state in the United States produces some wool (Texas supplies the most), it is not enough for the country's needs, and wool is also imported from other countries.

Sheep are usually sheared (their coats cut) once a year in the spring, when the animals no longer need their thick coats to keep them warm. In areas of the world where sheep are kept in large numbers, professional sheep shearers are employed, and they travel from farm to farm. Each worker can shear two hundred sheep a day using power shears. Each fleece, the coat of one sheep, must be removed in one piece. This makes the job of grading the wool easier because the wool at the front of the animal's body is usually of better quality than the wool at the rear.

After shearing, the wool is ready to be sent to the textile mill. There, it is carefully graded according to strength, fineness, the length of each strand, color, and crimp (waviness).

Fineness refers to the width of each fiber. The standard against which this is measured is the fineness of Merino wool. The length of each strand can be between about 1½ inches (3.8 centimeters) and about 2½ inches (6.5 centimeters). The fiber length is important because it is the main factor in deciding how the wool will be used.

The shortest fibers are called clothing length. These are followed by French combing length fibers and, longest of all, combing length fibers. The crimp is the quality in the fiber that makes it elastic, which means it will hold its shape well after being stretched and twisted. Color is important, too, because all wool must be bleached before dyeing, and obviously very white wool needs less bleach.

The general quality of the wool depends both on the type of sheep and on the individual sheep. The best wool, called lamb's wool, comes from sheep less than a year old. The first wool taken from a sheep between 12 and 14 months old is called hogget wool. Wool taken after the first shearing is called wether wool. Low-grade wool comes from sheep that have died or have been killed for meat.

Wool that has not been used before is called virgin wool. If the wool has been reprocessed or is being reused, the fabric is called shoddy.

Cleaning and spinning

New wool cannot be used until it has undergone a number of processing stages. The first of these is scouring. A sheep's fleece is dirty and covered with natural oils. It also contains seeds and burrs. All of

▶ *A sheep's fleece contains hairs of different length and quality. The longest fibers are coarse but ideal for producing smooth, worsted cloth. The shortest fibers closest to the body are softer and whiter and require less bleach to clean them.*

◀ Hand spinning of wool still takes place in some developing countries. It takes many years of practice to produce a smooth, even yarn that can be woven into a variety of fabrics or knitted to make garments.

Dyeing can be done at this stage, especially if the color must not run or fade, as in the case of men's suits. The sliver is straightened and reduced in thickness and goes through a process called roving, in which it is twisted into thinner strands.

Finally, the thread is ready to be spun into yarn. Yarn is made by twisting together several strands of a fiber. Wool yarn was spun at home for thousands of years, and the spinning wheel of the fourteenth and fifteenth centuries is often seen in old paintings. Wool yarn is rather fuzzy and thick, with the fibers running in a variety of different directions. Yarn is sold in balls or skeins.

Spinning stages

There are three steps in spinning yarn. The first stage aims to thin out the fibers, the second stage involves twisting the fibers into thread, and the third stage is winding the yarn onto bobbins.

Thinning out the fibers is called drawing out. Drawing out is necessary because the raw material comes in clumps of tangled fibers. Disentangling these fibers, cleaning them, and straightening them are all part of drawing out. In the later stages of the process, drawing rollers are used. Gradually, these rollers pull the fibers apart, and what was a flat ribbon of material becomes much thinner.

Combing (carding) is the final step in drawing out. This is done by moving rows of metal teeth through the fibers to straighten them, similar to a person combing his or her hair. Combing is especially important for fine and smooth yarns.

The thin strands of fiber need a little twist to hold them together. This step is called slubbing or roving and is done by moving rollers just before the final winding takes place.

Spinning machines

Several inventions in England in the eighteenth century took spinning out of the home and into the factory. The first of these was the spinning jenny,

these must be removed. The wool is washed in hot water containing soap and soda ash and rinsed in clean water. In this process, a greasy, protective substance called lanolin is removed from the wool, which is used in the manufacture of hand lotion.

Even after the wool has been scoured, the toughest burrs remain in the fleece, so these are removed by washing it in a weak solution of sulfuric acid (H_2SO_4) and drying it at high temperature. This process dissolves the smaller burrs and makes the larger ones brittle, so they can be removed more easily at the next processing stage.

After the wool has been dried, the next process is called carding. The wool is passed through rollers that have thin teeth to untangle the fibers and arrange them on a flat sheet. They are then formed into narrow ropes called slivers.

The next step depends on what kind of fibers are being used and what kind of fabric they will eventually make up. The shortest clothing length fibers are made into woolen yarn, which is rather fuzzy and is used to make tweeds and homespun materials. The longer fibers are used to make worsted, which needs regular, smooth yarn.

For worsted thread, the slivers of wool must go through a stage called combing to remove the shorter fibers. The machines that do this also straighten out the threads.

invented by English carpenter, weaver, and engineer James Hargreaves (1720–1778) in 1765. The jenny could spin eight to eleven threads at the same time.

The next big change came in 1769 with the invention of the flyer spinning frame by English inventor Richard Arkwright (1732–1792). The invention became known as the water frame because its drawing rollers were first driven by water power. Not until 1890 was steam power used.

The flyer spinning frame did the twisting and the winding in a continuous action. After the drawing out was completed by the drawing rollers, the yarn went to another section of the flyer. It passed through an eyelet and onto a bobbin and was twisted while being wound onto the bobbin. A flyer spinning frame is still used today, but it is quite different from the original invention.

The spinning mule

English inventor Samuel Crompton (1753–1827) came up with the next type of spinning machine in 1779. It was called the spinning mule because it was a mixture of two other machines, just as the mule is a cross between the horse and the donkey. The spinning mule had parts of the jenny and the flyer spinning frame in it.

In the mule, the drawing rollers had a carriage that moved back and forth. First, the carriage moved close to the rollers, and the yarn passed to the spindles in such a way that the fibers twisted together. The carriage then moved away, and the yarn was drawn out. This twisting and drawing out at the same time made the yarn more even than wool that was processed using other machines.

As the carriage began to move toward the rollers again, the coils of twisted and drawn yarn were removed by two faller wires. One wire guided the yarn onto a container called a cop, and the other kept the yarn taut as it was wound. The faller wires stopped moving when the carriage reached the rollers, and the whole action started again.

Weaving and dyeing

Once spun, the wool is woven into fabric or used to make carpets. Some is spun to be used as knitting wool. Wool can be woven into a variety of fabrics, ranging from the heavy materials used for outdoor clothes to soft, light fabrics. Worsted yarn is made into broadcloth, gabardine, or similar fabrics.

The yarn is sometimes dyed before it is woven, but it is often made into fabric first. It may then be dyed as a piece or printed with a pattern of dyes. Dyes were once made from plant extracts, but they are now usually synthetic (made from chemicals).

Wool tends to shrink when it is washed, so it may be treated to make it shrink before it is made up into clothes. Shrinking is usually done using water under pressure, which also helps the fibers lock together to give the fabric a smooth finish.

Wool is not always used in its pure form. It is often blended with acrylic or other synthetic fibers to make the fabric more durable, less expensive, and sometimes flame-resistant.

◀ *Wool fibers are porous, so yarns can be dyed to a wide range of natural and synthetic colors.*

See also: COTTON • DYE AND DYEING • FIBER

Writing tools

About 5,500 years ago, the ruler of Mesopotamia (present-day Iraq) had so much property and income from taxes that he had to find a way to keep good records of it all. Historians think that writing developed from his need.

Clay was used as the first writing material. Soft clay was rolled out into thin tablets, and marks were made on it while it was still damp. The clay was then dried in the Sun. The baked tablets held a lasting record of what was written.

The first writing was word signs made out of a few simple lines and drawn onto a clay tablet with a pointed stick. The Mesopotamians did not use a general sign for a group of objects, so they quickly accumulated a large number of word signs. Soon, there were too many signs for anyone to remember. To reduce the number of signs, the Mesopotamians used a main symbol for a group, such as sheep, and added a small sign to it to mean the class of the group, such as male, female, or child.

At this time, the instrument for writing changed from a pointed stick to a cut reed, which was used to carve the surface of the clay. This made wedge-shaped marks, called cuneiform writing, from the Latin word *cuneus,* meaning "wedge."

The Egyptians developed word signs, called hieroglyphics, to write down important events. *Hieroglyphics* is also the name given to the pictographic (picturelike drawing) styles of writing of ancient Asia Minor, Central America, Crete, and Mexico. Picturelike symbols can be of three different kinds. One kind is an ideogram, which is based on an idea of something. For example, the Chinese character for the verb *to carry* is a man carrying something. The Chinese way of writing is ideographic and takes many thousands of complex characters. It is written with brush and ink.

▲ *Young children should be encouraged to write from an early age because it helps communicate thoughts, furthers the understanding of language, and improves reading ability.*

Another kind of pictographic writing is based on phonograms. To give an example, say that the word for owl in a language has the sound of "m" as the main consonant. The phonogram for "m" in writing would be a word sign of an owl.

The third way of writing pictographically is called determinative. One example is the pictograph for a woman sitting down, with a group of other signs around her. The whole collection of signs is to be taken together as her name.

When the first paper was invented in Egypt about five thousand years ago, the hieroglyphics had to be changed so that they could be written faster. This was done by reducing the symbols to a few lines so they were hieratic, or cursive (rounded and joined together in each word), similar to modern handwriting.

The Phoenicians borrowed the best of both earlier systems for their writing. By about three thousand years ago, they were using a separate symbol for each consonant in their language, which sped up writing a great deal. However, they had no vowel symbols, so words such as *ship, shop,* and *sheep* would all have been written as "shp." The meaning of the word had to be figured out from the way it was used in a sentence.

Arabic writing developed from the Phoenician method of using symbols for consonants only. However, modern Arabic sometimes adds smaller signs to stand for the vowels.

WRITING WITH INK

First developed in the seventh century BCE, the quill pen dominated as a writing instrument for more than one thousand years. The quills were taken from the outer wing feathers of living birds. The left wing was favored for right-handed writers because the feathers curved outward and away. However, quill pens had their disadvantages. It took a long time to prepare them for use, and then they only lasted about a week.

Fountain pen

The first fountain pens were produced in Britain around the 1830s, but they used a plunger that had to be worked repeatedly to keep ink flowing. The basic fountain pen as we now know it was introduced by U.S. inventor Lewis E. Waterman (1837–1901) in 1884.

Modern fountain pens contain a reservoir of ink inside a cylindrical container of plastic or metal. The ink from it flows onto a nib, which is made of stainless steel or gold and has a thin slit in its point. A feeder device at the open end of the tube controls the flow of ink. A screw-on or press-on cap protects the nib and also prevents accidental leakage.

The action of a fountain pen relies on the surface tension of the ink. Surface tension has the unusual effect of causing liquids in a narrow tube to rise

▶ *This illustration shows a cross-section through a cartridge pen (in red and blue) and some examples of filling methods of other types of fountain pens.*

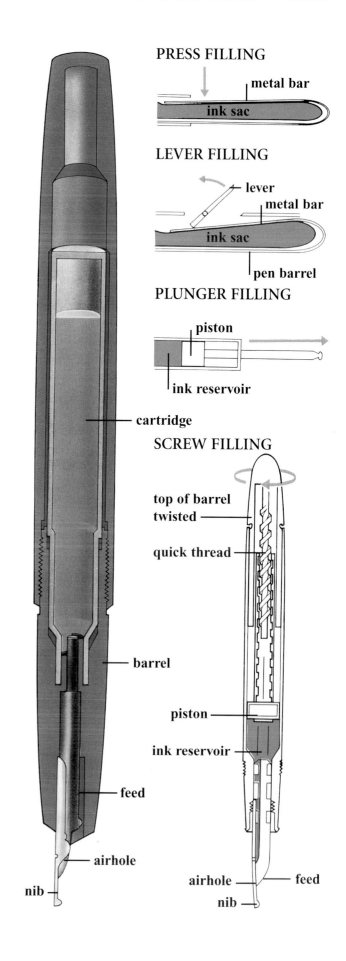

PRESS FILLING

metal bar

ink sac

LEVER FILLING

lever

metal bar

ink sac

pen barrel

PLUNGER FILLING

piston

ink reservoir

cartridge

SCREW FILLING

top of barrel twisted

quick thread

barrel

piston

ink reservoir

feed

airhole

nib

airhole

feed

nib

against the force of gravity. The ink in the pen's reservoir clings to the tube's walls until some ink leaves the open end—then it flows. Surface tension of the ink makes it flow down onto the nib to the slit and keeps the ink from running off the nib. When the nib is pressed against paper in the act of writing, the slit widens and releases the ink.

Fountain pens have different mechanisms for being loaded with ink. One type has a reservoir made of an elastic material, with a lever on the outside. With the lever pulled out to compress the tube, the tip of the pen is inserted into ink. When the lever is released, the tube fills with ink. Another type draws in the ink with a plunger used as a suction device. A third gets its ink from a cartridge. A cartridge is a replaceable plastic container of ink, which is the actual reservoir itself. It is put in by unscrewing apart the body of the pen. When the body is screwed together again, the lower end of the cartridge is automatically opened up.

Ballpoint pen

U.S. inventor John Loud devised the ballpoint pen in 1888. He used his pen for marking textiles, but it was never manufactured in large quantities. In 1938, Hungarian brothers László Biró (1900–1985) and Georg Biró patented a more reliable ballpoint pen. The following year, working from Argentina, they gave permission to companies in other countries to produce the pens. They were soon widely used in Britain and became known as "biros."

Modern designs

The ballpoint pen has a tiny steel ball at its tip. When the pen is being used, the ball rotates, automatically coating itself with ink. The ink is stored in a reservoir tube inside the body of the pen. The ink is too thick to leak out accidentally.

Although the ball of the pen is usually made of steel, other hard substances, such as tungsten carbide (WC) may be used. The ball, usually $\frac{1}{25}$ inch (1 millimeter) in diameter, is held in a socket. The

▶ *The fountain pen came into popular use in the late nineteenth century, replacing the quill as a way of writing with ink.*

back of the socket leads to a tube containing the ink. As the ink in the socket is used up, it is replaced by ink flowing down from the reservoir tube.

Early ballpoint pens often leaked because the ink they used was too runny. Modern designs contain a thicker ink made from a dye dissolved in oil or spirit. The oil-based ink dries quickly by being absorbed into the writing surface. Spirit-based ink dries by evaporation and gives sharper lines.

An opening must be provided at the far end of the tube for the ink to flow properly. If the tube is narrow, it can be left completely open. The thickness of the ink prevents it from leaking through the opening. Above the ink is a layer of an even thicker liquid called a follower. This is thick enough not to leak out but is just runny enough to follow the ink down the tube as the pen is used.

PENCILS

Pencils are thin rods of graphite, usually enclosed in a sleeve of wood. Pencils may be used for writing, but are more often used for drawing or marking. Unlike other forms of writing, pencil marks can easily be removed, by using a rubber eraser.

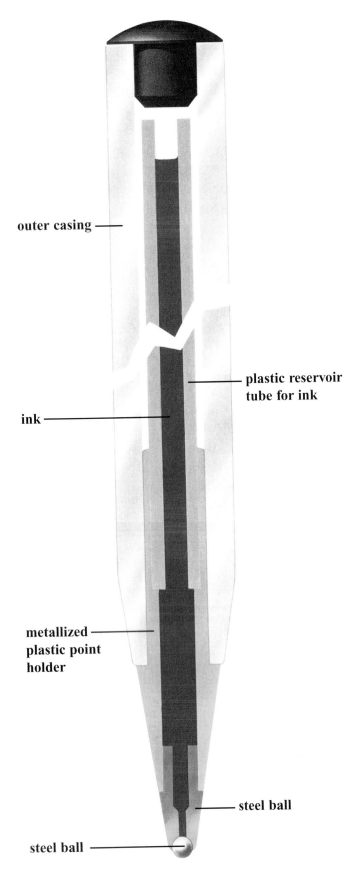

outer casing

plastic reservoir
tube for ink

ink

metallized
plastic point
holder

steel ball

steel ball

▲ *This illustration shows a cross section through a
ballpoint pen. Only the tip is made of metal.*

Although very simple implements, pencils were not invented until the sixteenth century, after an unusually pure deposit of graphite was discovered in Borrowdale, England, in 1564. Originally, graphite was thought to be a type of lead, hence the writing part of a pencil is still often called the lead. The darkness of a pencil mark depends on the number of tiny particles of graphite deposited by the lead on the fibers of the paper. A soft lead leaves a darker mark than a hard lead.

WRITING MACHINES

Although pens and pencils are still used as writing tools, many people started using typewriters and then word processors in the nineteenth and twentieth centuries.

A typewriter is a machine for printing words on paper. It is worked by striking keys with the fingers. As a key is pressed, it operates a linkage connected to an arm with a metal character (called a type slug) on the end. The type slug swings against an inked ribbon in front of the paper, marking the character on the paper. Any errors have to be covered with correction fluid, or the document must be retyped.

The introduction of electric typewriters made typing much faster and easier. Some electric typewriters have a lift-off ribbon that allows typing errors to be corrected. However, they do not provide for extensive editing, such as the insertion or deletion of words, sentences, or paragraphs.

A modern word-processing system consists of a keyboard similar to a typewriter keyboard; the central processor—the computer's "brain;" a screen similar to a television screen; a storage device known as a disk unit; and a printer.

The advantage of word processors is that the text is not actually printed out onto paper until the correct version has been keyed in. Once this has been done, and the full text has been entered into the computer's memory, the document can be printed out on a printer at the push of a button.

See also: COMPUTER • KEYBOARD AND
TYPEWRITER • PRINTING • SURFACE TENSION

X-ray

X-rays are a form of electromagnetic radiation. They contain a lot of energy and can pass through soft substances, including parts of the human body. X-rays are used to take pictures of inside the body and other objects.

In 1895, German physicist Wilhelm Röntgen (1845–1923) was doing an experiment with a piece of electrical apparatus inside a cardboard box. The room was dark, and Röntgen noticed that a nearby sheet of fluorescent paper glowed when the electrical apparatus was turned on.

Röntgen decided that the apparatus was producing a type of radiation that could pass through the cardboard box and make the paper glow. Because the nature of the rays was unknown, he called them X-rays. He later discovered that these same rays could also pass through paper, wood, and even aluminum. X-rays also made photographic paper darken, in the same way that light does. Most importantly, when he covered the paper with his hand, the rays passed through his soft flesh. Only the hard bones in the hand blocked the rays and cast a shadow on the paper.

What are X-rays?

X-rays are a type of electromagnetic radiation, similar to light and radio waves. They consist of waves of particles, called photons, that travel at the speed of light (186,000 miles, or 300 kilometers, per second). The wavelengths (distance between wave crests) of X-rays are short compared to most other types of radiation—between 0.001 and 10 nanometers (billionths of a meter). This is much shorter than the wavelength of light—about 500 nanometers. Because X-rays have such short wavelengths, they can pass through solid materials, such as the soft tissues of the human body. Light is reflected off the surface or absorbed by these materials.

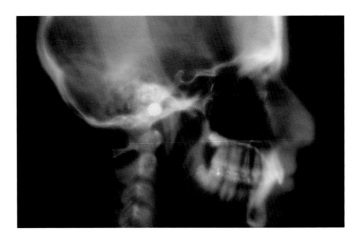

▲ X-rays pass through soft substances, such as skin and muscle, but they are blocked by harder substances, such as bone. Similar to light, X-rays make images on photographic film. An X-ray beam will make an image of the interior of the human body. The light areas are the hard bones, and the dark areas are soft tissue.

Producing X-rays

X-rays can be produced in a coolidge tube, which was invented by U.S. chemist William David Coolidge (1873–1975) in 1913. This is a glass tube with all the air sucked out to produce a vacuum. Inside are an anode (positive electrode) and a cathode (negative electrode). An electrically heated wire in the cathode produces electrons, which are fired toward the anode by the electric field between the two electrodes.

The anode has an area made of tungsten. When the electrons hit the tungsten, about 1 percent of the energy in the electron beam is converted into X-rays. These rays are released through an opening in the lead shield around the coolidge tube.

Some X-rays are produced when the electrons collide with free electrons in the tungsten. However, most of the X-rays are produced when the electron beam hits the tungsten atoms. When this happens, an electron from deep inside the atom is knocked away, and another electron drops into its place. This causes radiation of a fixed wavelength to be released. Atoms of tungsten and other heavy elements produce X-rays.

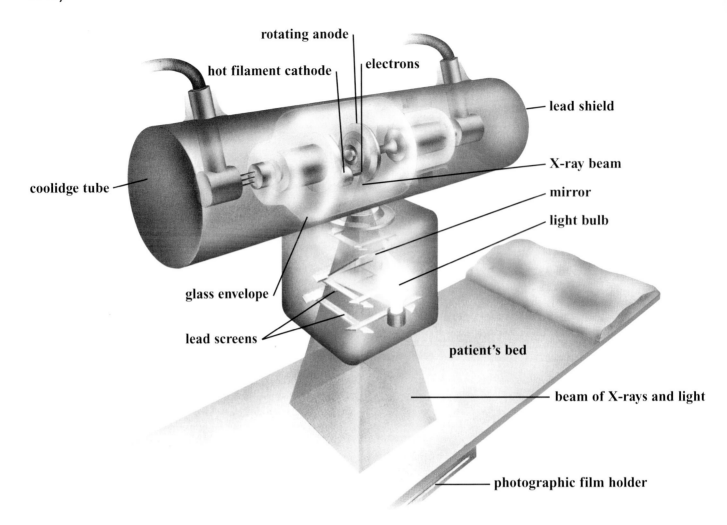

This illustration shows an X-ray machine that is used in hospitals. The X-rays are produced by an electron beam striking a spinning tungsten disk. A beam of light from a bulb lights up the same area that is being hit by the beam of X-rays. This helps the operator direct the beam into the right part of the patient's body.

When the electron beam hits the tungsten target, a lot of heat is also produced. Because of this, the anode has to be cooled with water. The anode is turned around at high speed, which also helps keep its temperature down.

Making X-ray pictures

Different body tissues absorb different amounts of X-rays. The denser the tissue, the more X-rays it absorbs. Thus dense, hard tissues form stronger shadows than softer ones. These shadows appear as white areas on the film. X-rays pass through the soft tissues and make areas of the film darken.

An X-ray image is called a radiograph, but it is also called simply an X-ray. Bones are the most dense body tissues, and they show up well in X-rays. These can show if a bone is broken and the position of a fracture. X-rays can also show blocked blood vessels, problems with organs, and arthritis in joints. X-rays are also used to locate foreign objects inside the body—such as a bullet.

Reading an X-ray correctly requires great skill. Doctors who are specially trained to do this are called radiologists. They must be knowledgeable about the way bones and organs look when they are normal so that they can judge any abnormalities correctly when they appear on film.

X-ray technicians, or radiographers, are people who specialize in taking radiographs. They prepare the person being examined to ensure that solid objects, such as jewelry, watches, and dentures, are removed to avoid producing a confusing X-ray image. The control panel of the X-ray machine is behind a screen to protect the technician. Taking X-rays is not dangerous for the patients, who have only a handful in their lifetimes. However, the technician must not be exposed often or the X-rays may cause health problems, such as cancer.

Studying internal organs

X-rays pass through the soft tissues of the body, so they do not produce an image of them. However, if an internal organ is filled with a liquid that keeps the X-rays from passing through, then an outline of the organ will show up on an radiograph. Such fluids are called contrast media. Generally, they include compounds of barium and iodine.

For example, an iodine compound injected into the bloodstream will cause blood vessels to appear dark on an X-ray film. This tells the radiologist whether any of the blood vessels are diseased.

Some iodine compounds, when injected into the bloodstream, are passed rapidly into the kidneys, down the urinary tract, and into the bladder. By taking a series of X-rays one after the other, the passage of the iodine can be followed, and any disease of the kidneys or other organs can be detected.

Barium sulfate ($BaSO_4$) is used to show all parts of the digestive system—from the throat to the rectum. A patient either swallows a "meal" of flavored barium sulfate, or the substance is pumped through the anus. The barium sulfate can then be followed down the body using a screen called a fluoroscope or by taking several X-rays.

A fluoroscope is a device that produces a steady stream of X-rays, which pass through the subject and hit a fluorescent screen, forming an image on the screen. Fluoroscopes are useful because they can make moving X-ray images. This allows doctors to observe many internal processes, such as the flow of blood through an organ, the swallowing action of the throat and esophagus, and the churning movement of the stomach.

▶ *Soft body parts can be made to show up in an X-ray by adding a liquid that blocks X-rays. The stomach and intestines in this X-ray show up because the patient has swallowed a liquid containing barium.*

Dental X-rays

X-rays are also helpful for investigating dental problems. Tooth decay is difficult to detect, especially in the teeth at the back of the mouth. An X-ray examination can clearly show decay, root disease, abscesses, and infections and can be helpful in selecting the most appropriate treatment.

Small pieces of X-ray film are held between the person's teeth. A low-powered X-ray machine, often mounted on the examination chair, is used to take the radiograph.

Computerized tomography

In the 1970s, computerized axial tomography (CAT) was invented. CAT scans use a line of several X-ray beams to make an image of a slice through the body. The beams all come from points along a curved scanner, which is turned around the head or another part of the body. After passing through the body, the strength of these beams is detected by receivers on the opposite side of the body. A map of that slice of the body is built up as the X-ray beams turn. The information is processed by a computer, and the result is displayed on a screen.

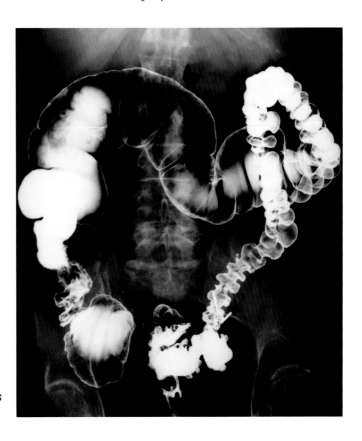

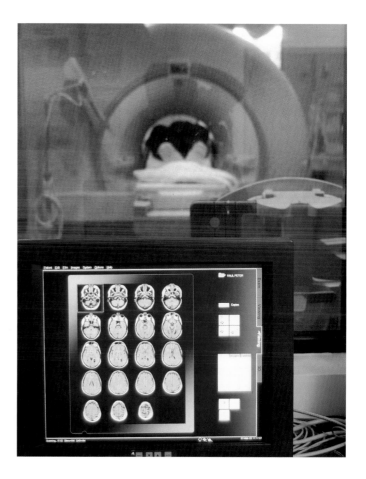

▶ *The large CAT scanner in the background makes pictures of slices through the body. A computer merges several X-rays to make the final image.*

Because the system is very sensitive, the CAT scans can show details of the soft tissues as well as the bones. For example, blood clots, tumors, and swollen tissue in the brain can be seen. Radiologists can make several scans in a series of slices that together produce a clear picture of objects inside the body. These can be put together to make a three-dimensional image.

Not only do CAT scans produce images in greater detail than conventional radiographs, the strength of the X-ray beams used by scanners is also much less than in normal X-ray machines. This makes them less risky for both patients and technicians.

The dangers of X-rays

The early users of X-rays did not bother to protect themselves or the people they examined. However, it soon became obvious that X-rays could damage the body. For example, skin was burned, and eyes became damaged. Later it was found that X-rays could also damage a person's genes. This led to cancers and growth problems in children born to mothers who had been exposed to X-rays.

An X-ray beam must be of the lowest possible intensity, while still being able to produce a useful image. Lead shields are used to protect any parts of the body that is not being examined.

Radiotherapy

As well as damaging healthy body parts, X-rays are also used to destroy cancers—a treatment called radiotherapy. X-rays are particularly lethal to fast-growing cells, such as cancer cells. Radiotherapy works best on certain cancers, often after surgery or before drugs are used.

Industrial uses of X-rays

X-rays can be used to examine the interior of pieces of machinery as well as the interior of the human body. Radiography is particularly important in examining the joints in airplane bodies. It is not usually possible to tell if the welding that holds the airplane together is faulty just by looking at it. However, with an X-ray examination, it is easy to see if any cracks have developed inside.

X-ray crystallography

Inside a crystal, the atoms form a repeating structure that is only a few tenths of a nanometer apart—much too small to see with microscopes. The wavelengths of X-rays are even smaller than the spaces in the crystals, so they can pass through the gaps. As they pass through, the X-rays spread out into a pattern by a process called diffraction. How they spread out depends on the size of the spaces inside the crystal. Chemists detect the X-ray pattern on a photographic plate and use it to figure out the exact shape of the crystal. This technique is called X-ray crystallography.

See also: CRYSTAL • ELECTROMAGNETISM • MEDICAL IMAGING • MEDICAL TECHNOLOGY • RADIOTHERAPY • SKELETAL SYSTEM

Yeast

Yeasts belong to a group of organisms called the fungi kingdom, which also includes the familiar mushrooms and toadstools, as well as fungi called molds and mildews. Yeasts are microscopic, round, single-celled organisms with many important uses, including the production of beer, bread, and wine.

Since ancient times, people have known that some foods and drinks undergo change if they are left exposed to the air. Sometimes the food or drink decayed and became inedible or undrinkable, but sometimes a change took place that improved the food or drink—both in taste and texture.

For centuries, no one knew what caused these changes. Then, in 1866, French microbiologist Louis Pasteur (1822–1895) made the discovery that the changes, called fermentation, were brought about by microscopic cells carried in large numbers by air currents. When honey and water or solutions of malt, apples, or grapes were left to become beer, cider, mead, or wine, they did so because of the fermenting action of yeast cells.

How yeast works

Of the many kinds of yeasts, the one most widely used in food is the cultivated yeast called brewer's or baker's yeast (*Saccharomyces cerevisiae*), used to make bread, beer, and wine. The cells are so small that it would take about four thousand of them laid in a line to measure 1 inch (2.5 centimeters). Each cell is capable of growing, reproducing, and performing the process of fermentation.

▼ *This colored scanning electron micrograph (SEM) shows a colony of baker's or brewer's yeast cells. Some cells in this picture can be seen dividing by rapidly budding off new cells.*

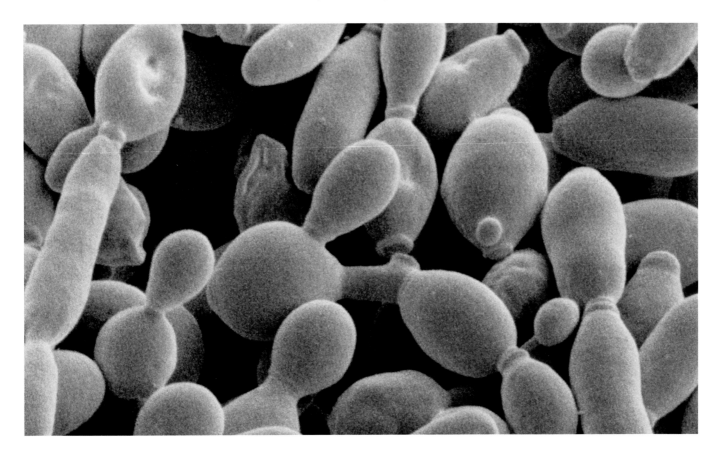

DID YOU KNOW?

Candidiasis is a vaginal infection caused by the excessive growth of the yeast *Candida albicans*. Doctors prescribe antifungal creams or drugs to treat the itching and burning symptoms of this unpleasant infection.

Fermentation

Fermentation is the process that occurs when yeast cells feed on sugar molecules. Yeast cells also need oxygen to breathe, and if they cannot get enough from the air, they break down some of the sugar into oxygen, converting some of the sugar into alcohol. This passes out into the surrounding fluid. As the yeast cells breathe the oxygen, carbon dioxide is released and rises as bubbles in the liquid or in solids such as bread dough. When all the sugar is used up, or when the alcohol in the solution becomes too strong, the yeast cells stop working.

Bakers exploit fermentation to bake bread. They mix baker's yeast cells with starch and put the mixture into the dough. The cells turn the starch into a sugar called glucose, which is used to make oxygen and alcohol. The yeast cells breathe the oxygen and release carbon dioxide gas, which makes the dough rise. When the bread is baked, the gas swells even more, making the bread light. The heat eliminates the alcohol and kills the yeast.

Other uses for yeast

Yeast cells are rich in protein, fat, and B-complex vitamins. Preparations made from yeast are used as a food supplement and as a source of vitamin B for both humans and animals.

See also: BREAD MAKING • CELL • FERMENTATION • PROTIST KINGDOM • VITAMIN

Yeast reproduction

Yeast cells reproduce by a process called budding. In certain places around the cell membrane of the parent cell, young yeast cells begin to form. Each of the new cells receives a nucleus—the dense center of the cell that contains a complete copy of the genetic instructions necessary for life. These genetic instructions organize the new cell so that it becomes an exact copy, or clone, of the parent. When the new cells are fully grown, they split off from the parent and are then ready themselves to reproduce by budding.

Zinc

Zinc is a bluish-white metal with many important uses. Pure zinc is not found in nature. It is combined with other elements as minerals. Sphalerite is the most important zinc mineral. It contains zinc and sulfur.

Zinc is not a very strong metal, and it is rarely used to make things on its own. Instead, it is mixed with other metals to form alloys. Zinc is often added to steel and copper to make useful alloys.

When heated above 212°F (100°C), zinc becomes soft, and it melts (turns into a liquid) at 788°F (420°C). At 1665°F (907°C), the metal boils (turns into a gas). This is a low boiling point compared to most other metals.

Zinc is a reactive metal. Before pure zinc is exposed to the air, it has a bright and shiny surface. Once it comes into contact with the air, the zinc reacts with oxygen in the air to form zinc oxide (ZnO). The zinc oxide forms a thin layer over the surface of the metal. As this layer forms, the shiny metal tarnishes, becoming dull and gray. However, the layer of gray zinc oxide protects the pure zinc underneath from further reaction with oxygen.

Making pure zinc

The first stage in making pure zinc from an ore, such as sphalerite, is to heat the ore in air. The zinc sulfide (ZnS) reacts with the oxygen in the air to produce zinc oxide and sulfur dioxide gas (SO_2).

▼ *Pure zinc is made by reacting zinc oxide with carbon. The zinc is cast into large bars, or ingots, that can weigh up to 2 tons (1.9 tonnes) each.*

The next stage is to use a chemical reaction to turn zinc oxide to zinc. This process is called reduction, because the zinc oxide is reduced to pure zinc and oxygen.

There are two main ways to reduce zinc oxide. The first involves boiling the zinc oxide inside a strong, closed container called a retort. The retorts are made of silicon carbide (SiC), which is a hard substance that stays tough even when it is hot. The retorts also contain pure carbon. Generally, this carbon is in the form of coke, which is made by roasting coal. The carbon reacts with the oxygen from the zinc oxide to form carbon monoxide gas (CO), leaving behind pure zinc.

Zinc can be reduced in a similar way inside a blast furnace. This process is called smelting. A fuel is used to heat the zinc oxide inside the blast furnace. The fuel used is coke. Zinc smelters are also often heated using electricity. Similar to the reaction

▼ *Sphalerite is the main zinc-containing mineral. It is made up of zinc sulfide. Sphalerite is often used as a zinc ore in the manufacture of pure zinc.*

inside the retort, the zinc oxide reacts with the coke to make carbon monoxide gas. The difference is that the coke itself provides the heat needed for the reaction to occur. The carbon monoxide gas also burns in the furnace once it forms, providing even more heat for the reaction. As it burns, the carbon monoxide reacts with oxygen to form carbon dioxide gas (CO_2).

The carbon dioxide sometimes reacts with the zinc vapor produced in the blast furnace. Unfortunately, this turns the zinc back into zinc oxide. This problem is solved by spraying melted lead into the zinc vapor as it rises to the top of the blast furnace. The zinc atoms dissolve in the molten lead in the same way that common salt (sodium chloride; NaCl) dissolves in hot water. A metal dissolved in another melted metal is called an amalgam. The amalgam is collected and allowed to cool. As it cools, the zinc rises to the surface. Zinc atoms are much lighter than lead atoms, so they float on the surface of the lead. The pure zinc is drawn off, and the lead is melted again and sprayed into the blast furnace.

▲ *Zinc oxide cream is used to protect pale skin from the harmful effects of sunlight. The white zinc oxide absorbs the invisible ultraviolet light that causes sunburn and skin cancers.*

Refining the zinc

Zinc made in this way is not pure enough for some uses, so it may be further refined. There are two common refining methods. Both are expensive, however, so they are only used when extremely pure zinc is required.

One method is called liquidation. The zinc is heated until it melts, and then the liquid metal is held at that temperature for several hours. Any impurities, such as lead or iron, in the zinc are still solid because they have a higher melting point than zinc. These solids sink to the bottom, and the pure zinc can then be drawn off.

A second method, called redistillation, involves boiling the impure zinc. Lead and iron both have higher boiling points than zinc, and cadmium (another common impurity) has a lower one. So it is possible to separate all the metals by collecting vapor produced at different temperatures.

Uses of zinc

One of the main uses of zinc is to galvanize iron. A coating of zinc is applied to the iron, which stops the iron from rusting in moist air. Galvanized iron is used to make objects that are often exposed to water, such as drains, gutters, and ship fittings. Zinc is also mixed with copper to make brass alloy.

Another important use of zinc is in die casting. Liquid zinc is squeezed into a mold so it fills every space. When it hardens, the zinc forms a precisely shaped object that does not need to be trimmed or reshaped at all. Many automobile parts, such as door handles, are made in this way.

Zinc oxide is a bright white substance. It is used to color paints, cosmetics, and soap. It also absorbs harmful ultraviolet light, so zinc oxide is used in sunscreen lotions. Zinc sulfide glows in ultraviolet light and is used to coat the inside of television screens and fluorescent lamps.

> *See also:* ALLOY • BLAST FURNACE • CASTING • CORROSION • IRON AND STEEL • METAL

Zoo

Zoological gardens, or zoos, are places where living animals are kept and displayed. The collections usually include mammals, birds, reptiles, and other animals from different parts of the world. Zoos give people a chance to see these animals at close range.

▲ *Zoos such as Central Park Zoo in New York City serve a vital function as places where animals can be studied by zoologists and conserved for future generations to enjoy.*

There are many different kinds of zoological gardens. Nearly all zoos exhibit a wide variety of animals from different parts of the world, but most specialize in keeping certain kinds of animals. Some, such as the Arizona-Sonora Desert Zoo Museum in Tucson, Arizona, display creatures from a small area—in this case, the Sonora Desert. It is only a small zoo, but the ways in which the animals are shown are so successful that they have been copied by other zoos around the world.

Since the 1970s, many wildlife parks have been developed where the animals are allowed to roam over large areas of parkland. The usual way of seeing the animals in such settings is to drive through the park in a truck or bus or to ride on a specially built railroad or monorail.

Purposes of zoos

There is at least one zoo in most major cities, and many others in the countryside. Zoos attract all age groups to see their collections of animals. They also help keep people aware of the wonders of nature and of the need to preserve wildlife from the natural—and human—dangers that threaten them.

In many zoos, educational tours are arranged for groups of schoolchildren. Large zoos often have a separate children's zoo, where young children are able to touch and even feed some of the animals.

Zoos are also places where zoologists (scientists who study animals) can learn about the habits of living animals in a scientific way. Another vital part of the work in many zoos is wildlife conservation.

Several species that have become threatened or endangered in their natural habitat are being bred in captivity. The hope is that one day some of these can be released back into the wild.

Zoo history

Animals have been displayed in zoos since ancient times. The first known zoo was established by Queen Hatshepsut of Egypt around 1500 BCE. Most of the early zoos were started by kings and emperors as a sign of power and wealth. The ancient Greeks, however, used their public zoos to teach students about animals and plants.

The history of modern zoos dates back to the sixteenth century, when European explorers brought strange creatures back from their travels. Many of these zoos were nothing more than a few bears, lions, and tigers kept in cramped and dirty cages or pits. As zoos have grown larger, the conditions for the animals have become much better.

The oldest zoo still open to the public is Schönbrunn Zoo in Austria, which opened in 1752. The first zoo in the United States opened in 1864 in Central Park in New York City. It is still there, and there is now also a children's zoo.

Caring for animals

Each animal species has its own special needs. Keeping animals healthy in the zoo, which is usually very different from the animals' natural habitat, is no easy task. Detailed knowledge of their habits and diet is needed to care for them properly.

Most zoos contain creatures from a wide variety of natural homes—ranging from tropical forests, deserts, and swamps to the polar ice caps. The larger, warm-blooded mammals and birds can often be trained to survive in the unnatural weather conditions of their surroundings in the zoo. It is not unusual to see polar bears and penguins outside on days that seem hot for them. Meanwhile, in nearby enclosures are elephants or lions, which might be expected to feel cold. However, some animals are more delicate, especially smaller mammals and birds and cold-blooded reptiles, amphibians, and fish. These animals often need specially designed enclosures that can be kept at the correct temperature and humidity.

How animals are displayed

In many modern zoos, the animals are shown in surroundings that look as natural as possible. There may be plants growing, as well as pools and waterfalls. Often there are beautifully kept gardens and tree-lined paths that guide visitors from one display to the next.

The life of animals in zoos is easier in many ways than it would be for them in the wild because they are given regular meals, protection from enemies, and good medical care. However, being kept in enclosures may be frustrating for the animals, especially if they live alone in small, uninteresting cages. By providing natural living conditions, zookeepers can encourage the animals to behave more naturally. Many wild creatures live in groups, and most zoos now keep several of the same species in the same enclosure where possible. Although many

▶ *Big cats, such as lions and tigers, are among the favorite attractions at zoos. Some species of tigers are now so endangered through loss of natural habitat that zoo breeding programs are the only way to ensure their survival.*

▶ *This young pygmy hippo is being kept warm under heat lamps and is fed special formula milk at regular intervals. Sometimes young animals have to be hand reared by zoo staff to ensure that they survive.*

animals in captivity, such as monkeys and apes, seem to enjoy being the center of human attention, others need their privacy.

Animals such as badgers, bats, owls, and raccoons are normally active only during the night. The Bronx Zoo in New York has developed a lighting system, now also seen in many other zoos, which makes it possible for visitors to watch the activities of these creatures. At nighttime, bright lights are shone in the cages, and the animals sleep because they think it must be daytime. During the day, the only sources of light are weak red or blue lamps, which the animals hardly notice, so they go about their nightly activities as usual.

Feeding

Providing a balanced diet to satisfy the nutritional needs of each animal is an enormous task. In the zoo kitchens, the staff prepare a wide variety of fresh foods, including eggs, fish, fruit, meat, milk, and vegetables.

Some types of reptiles, especially snakes, need feeding only at intervals of once a week or so. At the other extreme, some small mammals and birds would die of starvation unless they are fed several times a day. Some newborn animals need regular feedings of warm milk. In the wild, this would be provided by the mother, but frequently in zoos this feeding must be carried out by zoo staff. The staff may need to keep a constant watch to check that creatures are feeding properly.

Other animals have strange tastes in food. Many reptiles and amphibians will feed only on live earthworms and insects. Most zoos have special worm and insect farms to provide a regular supply.

Supplements to the diet include essential vitamins and mineral salts as well as any medicines prescribed by the zoo veterinarian. The quantities of food given to each animal are carefully controlled to ensure that every creature gets enough but not too much. Overfeeding may be a serious health problem

for animals in captivity because they do not get as much exercise as they would in the wild. The food given to each animal may vary with the seasons or according to other needs. For example, animals that live outside require extra food in the winter to keep them warm.

In addition to regular feedings, animals need clean bedding material. Their cages and sleeping quarters must be kept clean to prevent diseases from spreading. Pools of fresh water are provided for drinking, and often there are also larger pools in which the animals can bathe.

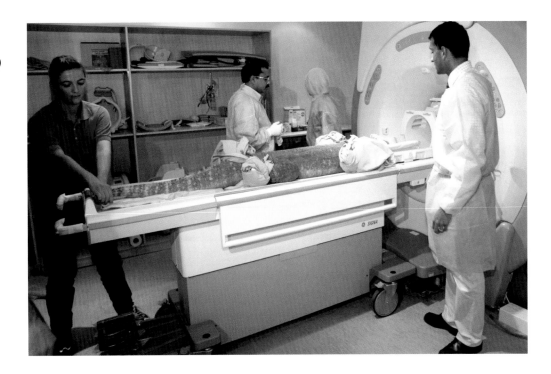

▶ *A Komodo dragon undergoes a magnetic resonance imaging (MRI) scan in a clinic at the Singapore Zoological Gardens. Modern zoos have the same type of facilities that are found in a hospital, including scanners, diagnostic laboratories, and operating theaters.*

Medical care

Although great care is taken to provide the zoos' inhabitants with the best diet and living conditions, sometimes an animal does become sick and needs medical attention. All large zoos have a fully trained veterinarian who checks the animals regularly. Sick animals are taken to an animal hospital where they can be treated. Some zoos even have operating rooms where surgery can be carried out if necessary.

Breeding

Living conditions for most animals in modern zoos have improved, and it is now possible to breed many species in the zoos. Most zoos have formulated a program to encourage the animals to breed.

Providing the right conditions for breeding requires even more care than keeping the animals fit and healthy. Creatures that are ready to reproduce must not be disturbed too much, so they are usually kept in quiet surroundings away from the general public and other animals. Suitable nesting material must be provided—straw or hay for most mammals; twigs and grass for birds to build nests; and soft soil or sand for most reptiles.

Male mammals are usually separated from their mates before the birth of the young takes place. It is not unusual for the males of many species to behave aggressively and even kill their own young. Sometimes mothers are not able to look after their young properly in the unnatural conditions of the zoo, so keepers must watch them carefully to see that all is going well. At the first sign of any problems, the young may be taken from their mothers and hand reared by staff in the nursery.

Where the animals come from

Until quite recently, most zoos relied on animal dealers for their supply of animals. The creatures were caught in the wild and shipped by plane or boat to dealers, who would then sell them to zoos. In 1975, however, the Convention on International Trade in Endangered Species of Wild Flora and Fauna (CITES) came into force. Administered by the United Nations (UN), CITES regulates the international trade in threatened or endangered wild animals and plants. More than 160 countries have joined the convention. Member nations meet regularly to consider adding new species to the treaty, to remove species no longer threatened by trade, and to make adjustments to trade rules.

See also: ANIMAL KINGDOM • BIODIVERSITY • BIORHYTHM • ZOOLOGY

Zoology

Zoology is the branch of biology that deals with the study of animals. These can range from microscopic protists to the blue whale—the largest animal on Earth. Recent research has shown that animals can communicate with each other better than zoologists had first thought. An urgent task is to protect many animal species from extinction.

▲ *A zoologist studies chimpanzee communication at the Language Research Center at Georgia State University, where the animals have been taught to "talk." By pointing to picture symbols, they can indicate objects and actions. Zoologists are debating whether this is similar to human communication.*

Zoologists are just beginning to figure out how different animals communicate with each other. Elephants use low-frequency sounds that can be heard by elephants over long distances but cannot be heard by people. Cetaceans (dolphins and whales) produce many calls to communicate with each other. Humpback whales "sing" to attract mates, and their songs can be heard at least 20 miles (32 kilometers) away.

Chimp talk

The animals with the most advanced forms of communication are the closest relatives of people, such as apes and monkeys. Although the grunts of East African vervet monkeys may sound the same to people, they seem to carry information, such as the approach of another group of monkeys.

Studying animals that have been raised with humans is not always a good guide to their abilities. Zoologists prefer to study groups of animals in the wild to observe natural patterns of communication. In the Ivory Coast, for example, zoologists have learned that some chimpanzees teach their offspring by showing them how to crack open palm nuts. It also appears that chimps can treat themselves when they are ill. They have been observed seeking plants that are known to contain antibiotics. When a chimp dies, its relatives will show grief, but there is no evidence that unrelated chimps in the group show any sympathy.

Mysteries of migration

Some animals show abilities greater than those of most people. Migrating animals, particularly birds and insects, cover vast distances with a great degree of accuracy. Many migrating animals use the Sun as a compass. They have some sort of internal clock, so they can allow for the Sun's daily movements. Birds can also use the stars for orientation, and maybe both butterflies and birds can feel Earth's magnetic field.

Many birds can find their way even if they are taken to a place off their usual route, so they must know the real position of their home site, not just its general direction.

Conservation

Conservation is an important part of zoology. Keeping a few animals in a zoo is not enough; there must also be suitable habitats in which they can live. Therefore, it is important to study animals in their natural environment to discover the normal requirements for food and habitat. Some animals eat specialized food and need a huge area within which to forage.

Modern scientific techniques are helping to improve conservation. Radio transmitters are fitted on collars while animals are temporarily immobilized. As the animals move, the signals can be traced by radio or even by satellites. Radio tracking is being used to study mountain lions in the United States. In the past, many animals were shot, and those that survived became confined to a few remote areas. Radio tracking has shown that each animal needs a territory of a size that depends on the amount of food available. Only a limited number of animals can live in a certain region. Fears that they would affect the numbers of deer and elk have proved to be unfounded. Most of the prey is too old or too young to be breeding animals.

Genetic fingerprinting can provide information on the amount of intermingling of different animals in the wild. Computer modeling can then show how many animals are needed to keep the species alive without losing the genetic range.

The living planet

Within an undisturbed ecosystem, the numbers of animals remain more or less the same. This is often called the balance of nature. If the climate changes, or if people kill animals or destroy vegetation, the balance is upset, and the whole ecosystem changes.

The distribution of the million or so animal species on Earth is uneven. On land, warm, moist plains have far more animal species than hot

DID YOU KNOW?

More than one million different kinds of animals have been classified by zoologists, but millions more remain unidentified, particularly in tropical rain forests. Because the forests are being cleared, many of these will become extinct before they become known to science.

deserts or cold mountain ranges. However, animals that adapt to even the most severe conditions are found in most parts of the world.

In the Northern Hemisphere, the polar regions contain creatures such as polar bears, while the seas are rich in fish and sea mammals such as seals. Farther south—through the tundra, the coniferous forests, and the deciduous forests of warm, temperate lands—the number of species increases. In tropical regions, the deserts contain a few highly specialized animals, while tropical grasslands are often full of animal life. Creatures that live in tropical forests are usually found in the trees because there is little food on the forest floor.

The oceans contain more types of animals than any other habitat. These include tiny zooplankton, which drift around in the surface layers feeding on microscopic plants called phytoplankton. In turn, the plankton provide food for free-swimming animals called nekton, which include 14,000 species of fish. Some of these are pelagic (living near the surface) and some demersal (living lower down). The oceans also contain the world's largest animal—the blue whale—and some of the world's most fearsome predators—the sharks.

◀ *An entomologist (zoologist who studies insects) demonstrates the attraction of female yellow-fever mosquitoes to his hand in an olfactometer. The olfactometer contains a screen to separate the attractant (his hand) from the mosquitoes.*

See also: BIOMES AND HABITATS • ECOLOGY • EVOLUTION • PARASITOLOGY • ZOO

Glossary

Aerodynamics The study of the way in which air moves around objects. An aerodynamic object is one with a shape that allows for a minimal disturbance of air flow around it.

Crank A device for transmitting rotary motion, consisting of a handle or arm attached at right angles to a driveshaft.

Drag The resistance of a fluid (a liquid or gas) to the movement of a body through it, measured as drag coefficient (C_D).

Equilibrium The state of a body or physical system at rest or in unaccelerated motion in which all acting influences are canceled by others, resulting in a stable, balanced, or unchanging system.

Fluorescent The emission of electromagnetic radiation, especially of visible light, given off by certain substances when they are irradiated by ultraviolet rays.

Gas turbine A rotary (rotating) engine that uses pressurized, burning gases to rotate (turn) sets of blades (turbines), producing continuous turning power.

Gear Toothed wheel used to transmit motion from one moving part of a machine to another. The teeth of one gear mesh with the teeth of another gear.

Genetic fingerprinting Method of isolating and making images of sequences of DNA (deoxyribonucleic acid). Also called DNA fingerprinting or DNA typing.

Gyroscope A mechanical device with a rapidly rotating wheel that stays pointing in the same direction in space even if its support frame is moved.

Ecosystem An interdependant community of living organisms functioning together within its nonliving environment as a unit.

Hydraulics The science and technology of the static and dynamic behavior of fluids, especially in relation to the control and management of water and the use of fluids to operate machines.

Inert An element that is not readily reactive with other elements and forms few or no chemical compounds.

Jet engine A gas turbine engine in which some of the hot, pressurized gases produced are ejected at high speed through a narrow nozzle at the rear of the engine to provide thrust.

Laser A device that generates an intense beam of pure electromagnetic radiation, which can, among other things, be used to cut through metal, perform eye surgery, and carry telephone conversations.

Latitude Part of the grid system used to locate points on Earth's surface. Lines of latitude form parallel circles around Earth, concentric to the Poles.

Mach number The ratio of an object's velocity to the speed of sound. Velocities below the speed of sound (Mach 1) are called subsonic; velocities above Mach 1 are supersonic.

Pitch In music, the position of one single sound in the overall sound range. Sounds are higher or lower in pitch according to the frequency of vibration of the sound waves producing them.

Radar Stands for *ra*dio *d*etecting *a*nd *r*anging. Equipment used to locate the position and velocity of distant objects using narrow beams of high-frequency radio or microwave pulses.

Resistance The opposition of a body or substance to electrical current passing through it, resulting in a change of electrical energy into heat or another form of energy.

Thrust The forward-directed force developed in a jet or rocket engine as a reaction to the high-velocity rearward ejection of exhaust gases.

Tsunami Large ocean wave usually produced by seismic activity on the seafloor.

Ultrasonic Referring to sound waves that have a frequency beyond the limits of human hearing.

Vaporize To change in physical state from a liquid to a gas, through heating and/or a reduction in pressure.

Velocity Rate and direction of the change of location of matter, measured in meters per second (m/s).

Wavelength The distance between one point on a wave to exactly the same point on the next wave cycle.

Index

Page numbers in **bold** refer to main articles; those in *italics* refer to illustrations.